# big NATE

## AND FRIENDS

# big NATE

## AND FRIENDS

by LINCOLN PEIRCE

SCHOLASTIC INC.
New York Toronto London Auckland
Sydney Mexico City New Delhi Hong Kong

ISBN 978-0-545-46801-5



12 11 10 9 8 7 6 5 4 3 2 16 17/0

Printed in the U.S.A. 23

First Scholastic printing, March 2012

IF YOU WANT TO IMPROVE AT MONOPOLY, FRANCIS, YOU'VE GOT TO PLAY HARDBALL DURING THE NEGOTIATING PERIOD!
OKAY... I'LL GIVE YOU ORIENTAL AVENUE FOR ILLINOIS AVENUE AND PARK PLACE!
1/1/97
THAT SEEMS FAIR...
NO! NO, THAT'S NOT FAIR!
© 1996 by NEA, Inc.
WANT ME TO THROW IN MARVIN GARDENS?
WAP!

YOU GUYS BOTH HAVE THE SAME PROBLEM AT MONOPOLY! YOU'RE TOO NICE! YOU NEVER GO FOR THE THROAT!
YOU'VE GOT TO BE RUTHLESS! WIN AT ALL COSTS! DO WHATEVER IT TAKES TO BEAT THE OTHER GUY! WHATEVER IT TAKES!
1/2/97
WANNA TEAM UP TO BANKRUPT NATE?
SURE!
© 1996 by NEA, Inc.
HERE, HAVE A COUPLE HOTELS!
THANKS!
HEY!

YYYYYESSSS! EVEN WITH YOU GUYS TEAMING UP AGAINST ME, I STILL WON!
THAT MAKES ONE HUNDRED GAMES IN A ROW THAT I'VE BEATEN YOU, FRANCIS! I AM THE MONOPOLY KING!!
ONE HUNDRED GAMES! THAT'S GOT TO BE A RECORD! LET'S ALERT THE MEDIA! LET'S CALL THE NEWSPAPER!
1/3/97
© 1996 by NEA, Inc.
I CAN SEE THE HEAD-LINES NOW!...
"BOY, ELEVEN, GETS TINY TOP HAT STUCK UP HIS NOSE."

LOOK AT THAT...
AT WHAT?
2/2
ISN'T IT WEIRD HOW EVERYBODY SPLITS UP AT LUNCHTIME?
THE BOYS ALWAYS SIT OVER THERE, AND WE SIT OVER HERE!
WE DO EVERYTHING ELSE SIDE-BY-SIDE WITH BOYS... HOW COME WE DON'T EAT TOGETHER?
THERE'S NO GOOD REASON I CAN THINK OF! C'MON, LET'S GO!
HI, GUYS! MIND IF WE —
BRAAAAAP!
WA HA HA HA
HA HA HEE HEE
HA HA HA HA HA
HIGH-FIVE ME!
I THINK I BROKE THE SOUND BARRIER!
HERE! PUT THIS CARROT UP YOUR NOSE!

AH, THERE'S NOTHING I ENJOY MORE THAN SPENDING A COUPLE HOURS IN THE COMICS STORE!
IT'S WEIRD, THOUGH. YOU NEVER SEE ANY **GIRLS** IN THIS PLACE. DID YOU EVER NOTICE THAT?
2/20
I MEAN, LOOK AROUND! IS THERE A SINGLE FEMALE IN SIGHT?
OH, YES...
OOOOOOOH! HEL-**LO**, RED SONJA!
© 1997 by NEA, Inc.

CALL 911! CALL 911! I'M HAVING A STROKE!
I CAN'T MOVE MY ARM!... IT'S PARA-LYZED! MY ARM IS PARALYZED!! IT.... OH.... WAIT A MINUTE...
I GUESS IT WAS JUST ASLEEP. YES, IT'S STARTING TO WAKE UP... I CAN FEEL IT TINGLING...
FALSE ALARM!
LET ME KNOW WHEN YOU FEEL A TINGLING IN YOUR BRAIN.
3/12
Peirce

YOU MAY HAVE THE HIGHEST IQ IN THE CLASS, FRANCIS, BUT I AM A TRUE GENIUS!
REMEMBER WHAT EINSTEIN SAID: GENIUS IS 1% INSPIRATION AND 99% PERSPIRATION!
I THINK IT WAS EDISON WHO SAID THAT, ACTUALLY.
3/14
EDISON, EINSTEIN... WHAT'S THE DIFFERENCE? THEY'RE BOTH DEAD INVENTORS, RIGHT?
© 1997 by NEA, Inc.
NOW HAND ME THAT DOO-HICKEY.
NO SWEAT.
Peirce

WE WERE TALKING ABOUT LEONARDO DA VINCI IN SCIENCE TODAY. MAN, WHAT A GENIUS!
DO YOU THINK IT'S POSSIBLE FOR SOMEBODY TO BE AN UNDISCOVERED GENIUS?
WHATTA YA MEAN?
4/27
I MEAN, DA VINCI WAS CLEARLY A GENIUS, AND EVERYBODY RECOGNIZED THAT, RIGHT?
YEAH...
BUT WHAT IF THERE WAS SOMEBODY OUT THERE WHO WAS JUST AS MUCH OF A GENIUS, EXCEPT NOBODY KNEW IT?
DOESN'T IT SEEM LIKELY THAT THERE ARE PEOPLE OUT THERE WHO ARE GENIUSES, BUT WILL NEVER BE DISCOVERED?
THERE MIGHT EVEN BE ONE OF THEM AT OUR SCHOOL!
HEY, GUYS!
WHAT'S UP? TALKING ABOUT ME?
LET'S HOPE NOT.
HEY, WHAT HAPPENED IN SCIENCE TODAY? I FELL ASLEEP.
© 1997 by NEA, Inc.

YOU KNOW WHAT I JUST REALIZED, FRANCIS? YOU AND I HAVE BEEN CLASSMATES SINCE KINDERGARTEN!
WE'VE ALWAYS HAD THE SAME TEACHERS! WE'VE ALWAYS BEEN IN THE SAME HOMEROOM! WE'VE BEEN INSEPARABLE!
5/8
EVERY CLASS, EVERY QUIZ, EVERY TEST! WE'VE BEEN THERE TOGETHER! WHAT A TRIBUTE TO OUR FRIENDSHIP!
© 1997 by NEA, Inc.
WHAT A TRIBUTE TO THIS SCHOOL'S LACK OF A "GIFTED AND TALENTED" PROGRAM.

WE SHOULD KEEP OUR RECORD INTACT, FRANCIS! LET'S TRY TO MAKE SURE WE CONTINUE TO TAKE ALL THE SAME CLASSES!
YOU MEAN ALL THE WAY THROUGH HIGH SCHOOL?
BEYOND HIGH SCHOOL! LET'S GO TO THE SAME COLLEGE!
WHERE SHOULD WE GO?
WELL, I MYSELF PLAN TO END UP IN THE IVY LEAGUE.
WHAT'S THAT? SOME SORT OF BOTANY SCHOOL?
I'LL TRY TO KEEP IN TOUCH.
9/5
© 1997 by NEA, Inc.

TODAY IS MOTHER'S DAY.
YUP.
WHAT DO **YOU** DO FOR MOTHER'S DAY? I MEAN, YOU LIVING WITH YOUR DAD AND ALL.
WELL, IT'S A LITTLE WEIRD...
MY MOM LIVES TWO THOUSAND MILES AWAY! ALL I CAN REALLY DO IS SEND HER A CARD AND CALL HER ON THE PHONE!
...BUT IT'S LIKE... I DON'T EVEN **KNOW** HER THAT WELL!
WOW. THAT **IS** WEIRD.
YEAH. I WAS SO LITTLE WHEN MY FOLKS GOT DIVORCED THAT I JUST DON'T REMEMBER MUCH ABOUT HER!
SO YOU DON'T REALLY EVEN KNOW WHAT IT'S **LIKE** TO HAVE A MOTHER!
NATE!
WHERE'S YOUR SUNBLOCK? WHERE'S YOUR CAP? IF YOU'RE GOING TO PLAY OUTSIDE, YOU'VE GOT TO PROTECT YOUR SKIN! HERE, PUT THIS ON!
I HAVE A VAGUE IDEA.
FOR LATER, I BROUGHT ALONG SOME NUTRITIOUS TOFU COOKIES!

HEY, FRANCIS! WANNA TEAM UP AND WORK ON THE SCIENCE PROJECT TOGETHER?
HMM... WELL, LET'S SEE... I CAN GET A TWELVE ON THAT PROJECT AND STILL MAINTAIN MY "A" AVERAGE...
I CAN'T RISK IT.
HEY!
5/20
© 1997 by NEA, Inc.
Peirce

WHAT'S UP, GUYS?
N.F.T. YARDCARE AT YOUR SERVICE, DAD!
WE'RE LINING UP CLIENTS FOR THE COMING SEASON! WE'LL MOW YOUR LAWN ONCE A WEEK FOR FIFTEEN BUCKS A POP!
6/2
WHY SHOULD I PAY N.F.T. YARDCARE FIFTEEN DOLLARS WHEN I CAN HAVE MY **SON** MOW THE LAWN FOR **NOTHING**?
© 1997 by NEA, Inc.
ANOTHER SLAP IN THE FACE OF SMALL BUSINESS.
RRRRRR
Peirce

HELLO, BOYS.
HI, MR. EUSTIS! WANT YOUR LAWN MOWED?
NO, THANKS! I MOW IT MY-SELF!
YOU DO? REALLY?
YOU'D BETTER BE CARE-FUL, MR. EUSTIS! PHYSICAL EXERTION CAN BE **DANGEROUS** FOR GROTESQUELY OVERWEIGHT FOLKS SUCH AS YOURSELF!
HE'S CONCERNED ABOUT YOUR WELFARE.
I'M THE GUY WHO PUTS THE **CARE** IN YARDCARE!
6/3
© 1997 by NEA, Inc.

HI, GUYS! WHAT'S UP?
WE JUST DID MRS. WINSLOW'S LAWN.
HOW MUCH DID SHE PAY?
THE USUAL... FIFTEEN BUCKS.
FIVE BUCKS FOR EACH OF US, EH?
WHAT?
"US"?
THIS MONEY'S OURS, NATE! YOU WERE SITTING IN SUMMER SCHOOL WHILE "N.F.T. YARDCARE" WAS WORKING!
7 27
HEY, THE "N" IN "N.F.T. YARDCARE" STANDS FOR NATE, IN CASE YOU FORGOT!
SO DOES THAT MEAN YOU SHOULD BE PAID FOR WORK YOU DIDN'T DO?
WELL, WHEN PEOPLE MISS WORK BECAUSE THEY'RE SICK, THEY STILL GET PAID!
THAT'S DIF-FERENT!
NO, IT'S NOT! WE'VE ALWAYS SHARED OUR PROFITS EVENLY!
I DESERVE MY CUT! GIVE ME MY CUT!
HOW'D YOU GET ALL THESE CUTS?
LAWN-MOWER ACCIDENT.

WHAT A GAME! FIVE TO ZIP!
YUP! I WAS AMAZING OUT THERE TODAY!
WE ALL WERE, NATE! IT WAS A TEAM VICTORY!
YEAH, BUT WHO'S THE STAR OF THE TEAM? ME!
9/28
I WAS A STONE WALL! I STOPPED EVERYTHING THEY SENT MY WAY!
BUT THE REST OF US SCORED FIVE GOALS!
SO WHAT? IT ALL STARTS WITH GOAL-TENDING!
LET'S FACE FACTS, GUYS: AS GOALIE, I AM THE BACKBONE OF THE TEAM!
WEDGIE.
NO! HEY! HELP!
FOR A BACKBONE, HE'S SURPRISINGLY SPINELESS.
PEIRCE

WHAT'S WITH YOU? YOU WERE STILL WORKING ON THE SOCIAL STUDIES QUIZ TEN MINUTES AFTER EVERYONE ELSE WAS DONE!
SO?
SO, IT WAS A TRUE-FALSE TEST! IT WAS TOTALLY BASIC!
NO, IT WASN'T! WHAT ABOUT ALL THE ONES THAT WEREN'T TRUE OR FALSE?
9/30
FOR THOSE, YOU HAD TO CREATE A WHOLE DIFFERENT CATEGORY CALLED "NEITHER," DRAW THE LITTLE OVALS, FILL THEM IN... IT WAS TRICKY, BUT I WAS ON THE BALL!
© 1997 by NEA, Inc.
HEY, DID YOU—
CONSIDER THE SOURCE.
Peirce

AH! OUR ANNUAL NEW YEAR'S EVE MONOPOLY GAME! IF MEMORY SERVES, LAST YEAR I DESTROYED YOU GUYS!
IF MEMORY SERVES, LAST YEAR YOU WERE ALSO IN CHARGE OF THE BANK.
HUH? WHAT WAS THAT?
12 29
WHAT'S THAT SUPPOSED TO MEAN, FRANCIS? WHAT ARE YOU IMPLYING WITH THAT REMARK?
JUST THAT IT'S UNUSUAL TO WIN WHEN ALL YOU OWN ARE TWO RAILROADS AND WATER WORKS.
HEY! HEY! I HAD THREE RAILROADS!
© 1997 by NEA, Inc.

IF YOU GET A THREE, A FOUR, A SIX, AN EIGHT, A NINE OR AN ELEVEN, YOU'LL LAND ON MY HOTELS! YOU'RE DEAD MEAT!
TWELVE!
AAAARRGH!..
A-ONE... A-TWO... A-THREE... A-FOUR... A-FIVE ... A-SIX... A-SEVEN... A-EIGHT...
12/30
YOU DON'T HAVE TO COUNT OFF EVERY SINGLE SPACE!
A-NIIIIIIINE...
Peirce

THE ONLY WAY YOU CAN ESCAPE MY PROPERTIES IS TO GET AN ELEVEN! YOU'RE GOIN' DOWN! NYA HA HA HA HA
BWA HA HA HA HA HA HA HA HA HA HA HA HAA!
12/31
NYA HYA HA HA HA HA HA HA HA —
ELEVEN!
© 1997 by NEA, Inc.
WA HA HA HA HA HA HA HA HA HA HA

HOLD IT, TEDDY!
WHOA! WHOA! WHAT ARE YOU DOING?
HAVING A SNOWBALL FIGHT WITH FRANCIS... AS IF YOU DIDN'T KNOW!
WHAT'S THAT SUPPOSED TO MEAN?
1/4/98
DON'T PLAY INNOCENT! I FELL FOR THAT LAST TIME!
OH. YOU MEAN WHEN I AMBUSHED YOU WHILE WORKING AS FRANCIS' DOUBLE AGENT?
DUH! YOU'RE OBVIOUSLY WORKING FOR HIM AGAIN!
YOU'RE JUST ASSUMING THAT! WHAT IF YOU'RE WRONG?
HUH?
HOW DO YOU KNOW I'M WORKING FOR FRANCIS? HOW DO YOU KNOW I'M NOT WORKING FOR YOU?
HMM... THAT'S RIGHT. MAYBE YOU ARE WORKING FOR ME...
HEY, BUT WAIT A MINUTE! IF YOU WERE WORKING FOR ME, WOULDN'T I—?
POW!
JUST FOR THE RECORD, I'M NOT WORKING FOR YOU.
CAN WE PLAY SOMETHING ELSE? THIS IS TOO EASY.

HEY, WHAT'D YOU GUYS PUT DOWN FOR NUMBER FIVE? I PUT "B"!
I PUT "B"!
I PUT "B"!
HMF!
LISTEN TO YOURSELVES! YOU'RE LIKE LEMMINGS! PERISH FORBID THAT YOU ALL DON'T GIVE THE EXACT SAME ANSWER!
YOU'RE SPOON-FED ALL THIS USELESS INFORMATION, AND THEN YOU SPEW IT BACK UP ON DEMAND! WHERE'S THE INDIVIDUALITY? WHERE'S THE IMAGINATION??
1/5/98
© 1997 by NEA, Inc.
YOU DIDN'T PUT "B," DID YOU?
DO WE REALLY KNOW WHAT YEAR BEN FRANKLIN WAS BORN? I MEAN, FOR SURE?
PEIRCE

UH-OH... I'M STARTING TO GET THAT FAMILIAR FEELING AGAIN...
1/9/98
I CAN'T CONTROL MYSELF!... I'M POWERLESS TO STOP IT! YES, I'M ABOUT TO HAVE A...
NOOGIE ATTACK!!
YAAGH!
© 1997 by NEA, Inc.
TEN TO ONE THEY DON'T TRY THIS STUFF IN MATH.
NOOGIE
NOOGIE
NOOGIE

WELL? HOW'D IT GO?
GREAT!
I NAILED HIM POINT-BLANK WITH THREE SNOWBALLS!
HEE HEE!
THAT'LL TEACH NATE NOT TO CHALLENGE ME TO ANY MORE SNOWBALL FIGHTS!
HE HAS ABSOLUTELY **NO CLUE** ABOUT THE ART OF WAR!
HE HAS NO CUNNING! NO BATTLE INSTINCTS WHATSOEVER!
LIKE THE WAY I USED **YOU** AS A DOUBLE AGENT! SHEER GENIUS! YOU THINK **HE'D** EVER THINK UP A PLAN LIKE THAT?
I'M NOT SURE...
WHY DON'T YOU ASK HIM?
YAAAA
COCOA?
LOVE SOME!
CLIK!

I'VE SIGNED UP TO BE A "PEER COUNSELOR"!
YOU? YOU?
1/26
NO OFFENSE, NATE, BUT I JUST DON'T SEE HOW YOU COULD POSSIBLY BE A PEER COUNSELOR!
I KNOW WHAT YOU MEAN, FRANCIS! YOUR CONFUSION IS COMPLETELY UNDERSTANDABLE!
HOW CAN SOMEONE WHO'S PEERLESS BE A PEER COUNSELOR?
YES, YOU'VE READ MY MIND.
PEIRCE

THE IDEA OF YOU, OF ALL PEOPLE, BEING A "PEER COUNSELOR" IS ABSURD!
1/27
PEER COUNSELING IS ABOUT RESOLVING CONFLICTS! TALKING THINGS OUT! YOU DON'T KNOW ANY-THING ABOU—
WAK!
YOU WERE SAYING?
YOU'RE A NATURAL.

WELCOME, EVERYONE, TO PEER COUNSELOR TRAINING! PEER COUNSELING IS ALL ABOUT EMPOWERING KIDS TO RESOLVE THEIR OWN CONFLICTS!
YOU'RE GOING TO LEARN TO USE POSITIVE COMMUNICATION TO KEEP SMALL PROBLEMS FROM BECOMING BIG ONES!
OUR GOAL IS FOR YOU STUDENTS TO WORK PROBLEMS OUT WITH NO TEACHER INTERVENTION! ANY QUESTIONS SO FAR?... YES...TEDDY?
1/28
© 1998 by NEA, Inc.
NATE KEEPS GIVING ME WEDGIES!
ONLY BECAUSE TEDDY STOLE MY CHAIR!
Peirce

THERE'S A BOY I REALLY LIKE...
BUT I LIKE HIM TOO!
BUT I LIKED HIM FIRST, MEG! YOU KNEW THAT!
PEER COUNSEL "LET'S WORK IT OUT"
I'M ALLOWED TO LIKE WHO I WANT! WHY ARE YOU BEING SO-
YOU'RE SUPPOSED TO BE MY BEST FRIEND!
GIRLS, GIRLS! THIS CONFLICT IS COMPLETELY POINTLESS!
I HATE TO DISAPPOINT YOU, BUT... CHUCKLE I'M SPOKEN FOR.
1 29
© 1998 by NEA, Inc.
NEXT!
PEER COUNSELIN "LET'S WORK IT OUT"

I AM **AWESOME** AT THIS "PEER COUNSELING" STUFF! I HAVE A REAL KNACK FOR COMMUNICATING WITH PEOPLE!
PEOPLE HAVE ALL SORTS OF PROBLEMS, AND **I** AM ABLE TO SEE WHAT'S GOING ON **INSTANTLY**! IT'S A **GIFT**! I REALLY THINK I'VE FOUND MY CALLING!... 'SCUSE ME A SEC...
BRENT, I'M GOING TO TELL YOU THIS BECAUSE NO ONE ELSE HAS THE GUTS: YOUR BREATH SMELLS LIKE A SACK OF DEAD FISH.
1/30
© 1998 by NEA, Inc.
YES, I'M A HEALER.
Peirce

IT WAS MY IDEA!
WHO SAYS I DON'T REME
YOU
THA TOTA
NO WAY!
YOU'RE WRITI PAPER THAT I
DID NOT!
ACTING LIKE
NO F
WHAT DO YOU THINK, NATE? WHO'S RIGHT, HIM OR ME?
WELL, YOU'VE BOTH MADE COMPELLING ARGUMENTS...
IT JUST MIGHT HELP ME MAKE A DECISION IF I HAD A LITTLE SOMETHING TO KEEP ME GOING!
OUR PEER COUNSELOR IS SOLICITING A BRIBE.
NOT A BRIBE, A TWINKIE! A TWINKIE!
1/31

THERE GOES "Q-TIP." MAN, DO I NEED WHAT HE'S GOT!
A TRUST FUND?
NO, YOU IDIOT! A NICKNAME! HAVE YOU HAPPENED TO NOTICE THAT ALL THE COOLEST AND MOST POPULAR KIDS HAVE NICKNAMES?
IF I CAN COME UP WITH A GOOD NICKNAME FOR MYSELF, MY "COOLNESS QUOTIENT" WILL SKYROCKET! I'LL BECOME ONE OF THE POPULAR CROWD!
© 1998 by NEA, Inc.
3/30
THIS SOUNDS EERILY LIKE THE TIME YOU TRIED TO PIERCE YOUR OWN NAVEL.
BUT THIS IS DIFFERENT! THIS CAN'T GET INFECTED!
Peirce

OKAY, GUYS, LET'S BRAINSTORM! HELP ME THINK UP A NICKNAME FOR MY-SELF!
US? WHY US?
BECAUSE THREE HEADS ARE BETTER THAN ONE! NOW COME ON! GIVE ME A HAND HERE!
3/31
HEY! MAYBE THE PER-FECT NICKNAME IS ALREADY OUT THERE! THINK, GUYS! HAVE YOU EVER HEARD ANYONE CALL ME ANYTHING?
F
OH MY, YES.
I'VE HEARD TALK OF GRAFFITI IN THE SECOND-FLOOR GIRLS' BATHROOM!
F

HMM... HERE'S A FOOT-BALL PLAYER WITH THE NICKNAME "SLASH"!
HE WAS NAMED THAT BECAUSE HE STARTED OUT AS A QUARTERBACK SLASH RUNNING BACK SLASH RECEIVER! PRETTY COOL, EH?
4/1
HIS NICKNAME IS A PUNCTUATION MARK! MAYBE I COULD COME UP WITH A NICKNAME LIKE THAT FOR MYSELF!
HOW ABOUT NATE "MINUS" WRIGHT?
I'VE ALWAYS THOUGHT OF YOU AS A "COLON."
Peirce

HAVE YOU EVER REALLY THOUGHT ABOUT HOW UNFAIR SCHOOL IS?
THE STUDENTS HAVE NO RIGHTS! IT'S THE TEACHERS WHO TELL US WHAT TO DO, WHEN TO DO IT, WHERE TO GO!
A BELL RINGS: WE GO TO HOMEROOM! ANOTHER BELL RINGS: WE GO TO LUNCH! ANOTHER BELL RINGS! WE GO TO SOCIAL STUDIES!
ALL THESE BELLS ARE THEIR WAY TO CONTROL US! THEY'RE THE GUARDS! WE'RE THE PRISONERS!
I NEVER THOUGHT OF IT THAT WAY...
RRRRIIINNNNGG
OOP! TIME FOR MATH!
NO! DON'T GO!
5/3
RRRRRRRRRRR
IGNORE THAT BELL! TAKE BACK CONTROL OF YOUR LIVES!!
OH, NATE! YOU'RE WONDERFUL!
RIIIIIIIIIINNNNNNNNGGGGGG
STAND YOUR GROUND!
NATE!... NATE!... NATE!...
NATE! NATE!
ZZZZZ
Peirce

'SCUSE ME... COMIN' THROUGH... 'SCUSE ME...
'SCUSE ME... OW! HEY, WATCH IT!... 'SCUSE ME... HEADS UP...
EXCUSE ME!... HEY, MOVE IT!... MOVE IT!... COME ON!... OUTTA MY WAY!
I'M FREAKIN' OUT! I'M FREAKIN' OUT!
"CORRIDOR RAGE."
© 1998 by NEA, Inc.

MAN! IT'S POURING OUT THERE!
DANG! WE CAN'T SHOOT HOOPS IN THIS!
BUT HERE'S SOMETHING WE CAN DO!
WE CAN LOOK AT MY WORLD-FAMOUS "CHEEZ DOODLE" COLLECTION!
LET'S START WITH THIS ONE! IT'S PERFECTLY STRAIGHT INSTEAD OF CURVED! PRETTY UNUSUAL, EH?
7 12
...OR HOW ABOUT THIS! FIVE DOODLES, MAGICALLY LINKED TOGETHER IN A CHEESY, CRUNCHY CHAIN!
HERE'S SOMETHING YOU DON'T SEE EVERY DAY! A DOODLE WITH A HOLE IN IT! I ALMOST FAINTED WHEN I SAW THIS!
*CHUCKLE!* THIS ONE'S FUNNY! IT'S SHAPED LIKE THE HEAD OF ABE LINCOLN! UNCANNY, HUH?
NOW, IF CHEEZ DOODLES COULD TALK, THIS NEXT ONE WOULD HAVE QUITE A STORY TO —
?

HEY, HEY! LET'S HIT THE ARCADE!
WHAT'S THAT FOR?
THIS IS MY CARTOONIST'S NOTEBOOK! I TAKE IT WITH ME WHEREVER I GO!
WHY, YOU ASK? SO WHEN I SEE SOMETHING FUNNY HAPPEN, I CAN QUICKLY WRITE IT DOWN TO USE LATER IN A CARTOON!
THERE'S NOTHING A CARTOONIST HATES MORE THAN FORGETTING A GOOD IDEA! THIS WAY, I FORGET NOTHING!
NYAAAAA
WO WO WO
bump
bump
bump
bump
GAAAA
TONK!
RRRRIP
SPLAT!
WANT ME TO WRITE THAT DOWN FOR YOU?
FORGET IT.

HIKE!
WRIGHT
CHIPS
MUNCH
MUNCH
MUNCH
SLAM!
PERHAPS YOU MISUNDERSTOOD ME WHEN I SAID "GO LONG."
I DIDN'T WANT TO PLAY ANYMORE.

1/8/99
noogie noogie
noogie
noogie
ANOTHER RESOLUTION BROKEN!
YOU'RE NOT EVEN TRYING!
F
Peirce

$
© 1999 by NEA, Inc.
!
NOOOOOO
DID YOU HEAR A.... A PRIMAL SCREAM?
THE SNACK MACHINE MUST BE OUT OF "CHEEZ DOODLES" AGAIN.

PASS! PASS!
WHUMP!
PTOO!
STOMP!!
!
Yinnnngg
oof!
grunt!
zinngggggg.
FWING!
SLUP!
SWISH!
JUST THE WAY I DIAGRAMMED IT.
I GET AN ASSIST FOR THAT, RIGHT?

I'VE GIVEN UP THE TROMBONE! IT'S NOT HELPING ME GET GIRLS AT **ALL!** I'M GONNA TAKE UP A **DIFFERENT** INSTRUMENT!
GUITAR?
NO, THAT HURTS MY FINGERS.
SAXOPHONE?
TOO MANY KEYS.
3/13
TRUMPET?
NO, NO! AN INSTRUMENT THAT'S **EASY** TO PLAY BUT WILL **STILL** ATTRACT THE BABES LIKE MOTHS TO A FLAME!
© 1999 by NEA, Inc.
A DRUMROLL, PLEASE.
THE KAZOO!
PEIRCE

TOUCH-DOWN!
NO WAY! THAT'S NOT A TOUCH-DOWN! IT'S NOT OVER THE EDGE!
YES, IT IS! IT CLEARLY IS!
IT ISN'T! IT'S NOT OVER THE EDGE! IT'S DEFINITELY NOT OVER THE EDGE!
I will not play table football during class.
...BUT SHE IS.

IF YOU WANT TO EARN MORE MERIT BADGES, I'D SUGGEST YOU START WITH THE "HELPING HAND" BADGE! THAT'S AN EASY ONE!
4/6
ALL YOU NEED TO DO IS FIND SOMEBODY IN NEED AND LEND THAT PERSON A HAND! IT'S AS SIMPLE AS THAT!
SHOVE!
HELP YOU UP?
THAT'S NOT THE WAY IT WORKS!

HEY, UGLY!
HI, STUPID!
WHAT'S UP, GEEK-FACE?
NOT MUCH, BRAINLESS!
ARE YOU SURE, PENCIL NECK?
ABSOLUTELY, CHEEZ DOODLE BREATH!
5/17
WA HA HA HA H
A HA HA HA HA
A HA HA HA HA
© 1999 by NEA, Inc.
MALE BONDING.
HIGH-FIVE ME, PINHEAD!
Peirce

HERE, I BROUGHT YOU THE HOMEWORK.
*COUGH* THANKS. THIS COLD'S A NASTY ONE.
NOTICE IT'S ALWAYS KIDS WHO GET SICK? HOW COME MRS. GODFREY CAN'T COME DOWN WITH SOMETHING ONCE IN A WHILE?
5/20
WHOA, WAIT A MINUTE! IDEA! BRILLIANT IDEA!
WHAT?
HERE, SNEEZE INTO THIS CUP.
OKAY. COME A LITTLE CLOSER.
© 1999 by NEA, Inc.
PEIRCE

5/23
THIS IS DRIVING ME CRAZY! I'VE HAD THIS SONG GOING THROUGH MY HEAD ALL DAY AND I CAN'T GET RID OF IT!
WHAT SONG?
NO! DON'T SAY IT!
THEN WE'LL BE INFECTED, TOO! I DON'T WANT SOME SONG STUCK IN MY HEAD!
HEY, I CAN SAY IT IF I WANT TO! IT'S...
NO!... OH SAY CAN YOU SEEE...
...BY THE DAWN'S EARLY LIIIIGHT...
WHAT SO PROUDLY WE HAILED...
OKAY. WHATEVER.
HA! SHOWED HIM!
WHOSE BROAD STRIPES AND BRIGHT STARS...
THRU THE PERILOUS FIGHT...
I'M AS PATRIOTIC AS THE NEXT GUY, BUT THIS IS RIDICULOUS.
...AND THE ROCKETS RED GLARE...

HEY! CRUNCH WANNA PLAY CATCH?
NO! THAT'S ALL WE EVER DO! I'M SICK OF PLAYING CATCH!
IT'S LIKE EATING THE SAME FOOD DAY AFTER DAY! AFTER A WHILE YOU CAN'T **STAND** IT ANYMORE!
6/29
MUNCH
CRUNCH
CHOMPF
WHATTA YA MEAN?
I KEEP FORGETTING HIS "CHEEZ DOODLES" CONSUMPTION RECORD.
© 1999 by NEA, Inc.

HIYA, FRANCIS, OL' PAL! I'M BACK FROM CHESS CAMP! WHAT'S BEEN HAPPENING AROUND THIS BURG?
DID YOU GUYS MISS ME? HOW'S OUR BASEBALL TEAM DOING? HAS JENNY ASKED ABOUT ME? DID-
7/29
THIS IS NATE, YOU PINHEAD!!
OH, RIGHT. AND YOU SAY YOU'VE BEEN AWAY?
© 1999 by NEA, Inc.
PEIRCE

AH! THE COUNTY FAIR! THE HIGHLIGHT OF THE WHOLE SUMMER!
YOU SAID IT!
AND THIS YEAR, I'M GONNA GO ON EVERY SINGLE RIDE! I'M GONNA DO 'EM ALL!
8/9
BUT FIRST... THE **HOT DOG EATING CONTEST!**
© 1999 by NEA, Inc.
YOU'RE SITTING NEXT TO HIM ON THE ZIPPER.
AM NOT.
NARF NARF NARF NARF
DO

WELL, LADIES, NOBODY ELSE IS GOING IN, BUT I WILL!
ARE YOU NUTS, NATE? THE WATER'S FREEZING!
OH, LET HIM GO, TEDDY.
HE'S JUST TRYING TO SHOW THE GIRLS HOW COOL HE IS!
8/17
© 1999 by NEA, Inc.
MISSION ACCOMPLISHED!
A... A... B-B-BIT... B-B-B.. B-BRISK...

BZZZZZ
BZZZZZZ
9/11
BZZZ
ZZZZ
BZZZ
MAY I CHANGE SEATS?
WHA-? HEY, I AM **NOT** COPYING!
Peirce
© 1999 by NEA, Inc.

HIKE!
OOP!
PSST! GUYS! TIMEOUT!
9/12
WHAT IS IT?
GROUP OF CUTE GIRLS AT TWELVE O'CLOCK!
OOOOH! REAL CUTE!
MAJOR CHANCE TO IMPRESS THE LADIES!
TIME TO SHOW SOME SKIN!
I'LL RUN A POST PATTERN AND MAKE A SPECTACULAR GRAB!
WHOA! WE'RE ALL PLAYING! WHY SHOULD YOU BE THE ONLY ONE THEY NOTICE?
BECAUSE I'M THE BEST PLAYER, FOOL!
HEY, I'M A MUCH BETTER RECEIVER THAN YOU ARE! JUST GIVE ME THE...
...BALL.

PLINK!
THANKS.
SURE.
9/19
PLINK!
THANKS.
UH-HUH.
PLINK!
THANKS.
grumble
PLINK!
MAY I MAKE A SUGGESTION?
STAY!... STAY!
Peirce

WANNA HIT THE ARCADE AFTER SCHOOL?
CAN'T, TEDDY. I'VE GOT DETENTION.
JUST ANOTHER CASE OF A POOR, INNOCENT STUDENT BEING BEATEN DOWN BY "THE MAN"!
9/20
"THE MAN"?
MRS. GODFREY.
SO YOU'RE SPEAKING METAPHORICALLY.
MAYBE, MAYBE NOT. CHECK OUT THE MUSTACHE.
PEIRCE

ODDS.
EVENS.
YES!
DANG!
I'LL TAKE ROBBY.
WHEN ASSEMBLING A DODGE BALL TEAM, THE FIRST DRAFT PICK IS CRUCIAL.
10/8
© 1999 by NEA, Inc.
Peirce

...AND SO I ONLY FINISHED HALF THE TEST! I COULDN'T HELP IT! MY BRAIN JUST STARTED GOING CRAZY!
I WAS TRYING TO THINK!... BUT THE NEXT THING I KNEW, I WAS MAKING UP ALL SORTS OF WEIRD LITTLE RHYMES INSIDE MY HEAD!
10/22
YOU KNOW HOW, WHEN YOU'RE TRYING TO CONCENTRATE ON SOMETHING REALLY BORING, YOUR MIND JUST STARTS TO DO SOMETHING ELSE?
98... 99... ONE HUNDRED SESAME SEEDS! 101... 102...
HEY! HEY! FOCUS! FOCUS!
SNAP SNAP
© 1999 by NEA, Inc.

OKAY, FRANCIS, SO YOU'VE GOT A STRAIGHT "A" AVERAGE! YOU'RE WHAT IS CALLED "BOOK SMART"!
...BUT I'M A DIFFERENT KIND OF SMART! I'M SAVVY! I'M SHREWD!
11 23 99
YES, I AM WHAT YOU CALL STREET SMART!
© 1996 by NEA, Inc.
BEFORE YOU HIT THE STREET, YOU MIGHT WANT TO MASTER THE SIDEWALK!
OOL
ZONE

AH! OUR ANNUAL NEW YEAR'S EVE MONOPOLY GAME!
THE PERFECT WAY TO RING IN THE NEW MILLEN-NIUM!
EXCEPT IT ISN'T A NEW MILLENNIUM! TECHNICALLY, THE NEXT MILLENNIUM DOESN'T BEGIN UNTIL 2001!
YEAH, YEAH. HERE HE GOES AGAIN.
WELL, IT'S TRUE! I'M JUST RELATING THE FACTS, THAT'S ALL! WE'RE STILL A YEAR AWAY FROM THE NEXT MILLENNIUM! WHY CAN'T PEOPLE SEE THAT?
12/30
SPEAKING FOR THE PEOPLE... BECAUSE YOU BORE US!
ALSO SPEAKING FOR THE PEOPLE, I'LL SECOND THAT.
© 1999 by NEA, Inc.

MY TURN! OKAY, I'M GONNA BUILD!
HERE... AND HERE... AND HERE...
12/31
WHOA, WHOA! WAIT! HOLD IT!
WHAT?
YOU CAN'T BUILD HOTELS ON RAIL-ROADS!
NOT UNLESS YOU'RE AN ENTREPRE-NEURIAL VISIONARY.
© 1999 by NEA, Inc.

HEY, FRANCIS! GIVE ME A HAND!
WHAT ARE YOU DOING?
WHAT DOES IT **LOOK** LIKE? I'M PREPARING FOR THE MOTHER OF ALL SNOWBALL FIGHTS!
HELP ME BUILD UP MY SUPPLY OF AMMO!
OKAY!
THAT'S IT! KEEP MAKIN' 'EM! YOU CAN NEVER HAVE TOO MANY SNOWBALLS!
2/20
WHAT AN ARSENAL!
I THINK WE'RE READY TO START THE BATTLE!
SCOUT OUT THE AREA AND SEE IF YOU CAN SPOT THE ENEMY!
RIGHT!
?
SAY, WHO **IS** THE—?
POW!
TAP TAP TAP
FORT NATE
Peirce

HOW MUCH WILL YOU GIVE ME IF I HIT THAT TREE?
THAT TREE? IT'S LIKE A HUNDRED YARDS AWAY!
WILL YOU GIVE ME TEN BUCKS?
NO, I WON'T GIVE YOU TEN BUCKS!
FIVE BUCKS?
3/12
I DON'T HAVE ANY MONEY! BESIDES, YOU COULD NEVER REACH THAT TREE!
HOW ABOUT THIS:
IF I HIT THAT TREE WITH THIS SNOWBALL, I GET TO HIT YOU WITH ANOTHER SNOWBALL!
FINE. YOU WON'T HIT THAT TREE IN A MILLION YEARS.
HERE GOES.
POW!
BY GOLLY, YOU'RE RIGHT! I WASN'T EVEN CLOSE!
peirce

OOH! DIBS ON THIS CHAIR!
NO, I CALLED DIBS ON IT!
BOYS! BOYS!
UNFORTUNATELY FOR BOTH OF YOU, I ALREADY CALLED DIBS ON THIS ENTIRE TABLE!
6/6
WHAT? YOU CAN'T CALL DIBS ON A WHOLE TABLE!
SURE I CAN! AND THAT GIVES ME DE FACTO DIBS ON THE CHAIRS AROUND THE TABLE!
© 2000 by NEA, Inc.
♪
"DE FACTO DIBS"?
I'M CALLING DIBS ON HIS SKULL.
COMIX

HEY, **HERE'S** A SWITCH! **I** DID THE HOMEWORK LAST NIGHT, BUT **YOU** GUYS PUT IT OFF UNTIL TODAY!
NOW **YOU'RE** SLAVING AWAY DURING OUR STUDY HALL WHILE **I** KICK BACK AND **RELAX**!!
6/10
WOW, I'M... I'M JUST NOT USED TO HAVING ALL THIS **FREE TIME**!
I DON'T KNOW WHAT TO DO WITH MYSELF!
HERE'S AN IDEA...
© 2000 by NEA, Inc.

WHERE'VE YOU BEEN? WE WERE SUPPOSED TO GO TO THE ARCADE!
I HAD DETENTION.
6/24
DETENTION? ON THE LAST DAY OF SCHOOL?
HEH HEH
HEE HEE... YUP.
WA HA HA HA HA HA HA HA HA
THERE'S SO MUCH I JUST DON'T GET.
HEE HEE! OH, MAN!
HIGH FIVE ME!
© 2000 by NEA, Inc.

OKAY, SO WE HAVEN'T BEEN ABLE TO FIND A NEW TROOP LEADER! I SAY WE JUST KEEP GOING!... WITHOUT A TROOP LEADER!
IT'S AGAINST JUNIOR WOODCHUCK BYLAWS, BUT SO WHAT? IS SOMEBODY GONNA REPORT US?
AHEM!
MAY I REMIND YOU THAT, IN ADDITION TO BEING COURTEOUS, HUMBLE, KIND, GENEROUS AND BRAVE, A JUNIOR WOODCHUCK IS ALSO HONEST!
SOMEBODY'S GONNA REPORT US.
GOOD JOB, FRANCIS. YOU'RE CLOSING IN ON THAT "WUSS-BOY" MERIT BADGE.
7/1
© 2000 by NEA, Inc.
Peirce

ANY LUCK?
NOPE. I CAN'T FIND ANY-BODY TO BE OUR TROOP LEADER.
DANG! WE COULD LOSE OUR CHARTER!
THERE'S GOT TO BE SOME ADULT OUT THERE WHO'LL DO IT!
7/3
WELL, GUYS, I JUST ASKED MRS. GODFREY TO BE OUR TROOP LEADER.
© 2000 by NEA, Inc.
SHE SAID NO!... URK!... SHE SAID NO!!
BUT YOU ASKED HER!... YOU ASKED HER!!
Peirce

I CAN'T BELIEVE YOU ASKED MRS. GODFREY TO BE OUR TROOP LEADER! THANK GOODNESS SHE SAID NO!
CAN YOU IMAGINE GOING CAMPING WITH THAT WOMAN? WOULD YOU WANT TO PLACE YOUR LIFE IN HER HANDS?
7/4
I WOULDN'T WANT TO BE STUCK IN THE WOODS WITH HER, I'LL TELL YOU! WHAT IF WE GOT LOST? WHAT IF WE RAN OUT OF FOOD, HUH? HAVE YOU CONSIDERED THAT?
I CAN SEE IT ALL NOW: SHE SUCKS DOWN ALL THE BEEF JERKY, AND TEN MINUTES LATER SHE'S RESORTING TO CANNIBALISM.
"JERKY" JUST ABOUT SUMS IT UP.
Peirce
© 2000 by NEA, Inc.

OKAY, OKAY, SO MAYBE ASKING MRS. GODFREY TO BE OUR TROOP LEADER WAS A BAD IDEA.
THERE'S AN UNDER-STATEMENT.
IT WAS AN IDIOTIC IDEA!
HEY!... HEY! I JUST THOUGHT OF SOME-THING!
7/5
WE KNOW PLENTY OF OTHER TEACHERS! WHY DON'T WE ASK ONE OF THEM? ONE WE ACTUALLY LIKE?
NOW THAT'S A GOOD IDEA!
© 2000 by NEA, Inc.
... A MUCH BETTER IDEA THAN ASKING MRS. GODFREY.
...WHICH WAS TOTALLY BONEHEADED.
WE'VE ESTAB-LISHED THAT!
Peirce

WHAT'S THAT?
A COOL BOOK! "MATH-TASTIC MIND BENDERS"!
BUT... IT'S SUMMER!
IT'S FUN! SOME OF THESE ARE SO HARD!
8/7
BUT IT'S SUMMER!
I JUST LIKE TO IMPROVE MY MIND!...
BUT IT'S SUM-MER!
...SOMETHING YOU MIGHT WANT TO CONSIDER.
Peirce
© 2000 by NEA, Inc.

AH, THE COUNTY FAIR!
SMELL THAT FRIED DOUGH!
MMM! COTTON CANDY!
HEY, WITH ALL THIS GREAT FOOD AROUND, WHY'D YOU BRING A LUNCH BAG?
THIS? THIS IS NOT A LUNCH BAG!...
8/14
THIS IS A "LOSE YOUR LUNCH" BAG!
© 2000 by NEA, Inc.
RIDE THE ZIPPER!
WHO'S WITH ME?
HE IS

STEP RIGHT UP! TRY THE GUT-BUSTER!
HMMM...
GUT BUSTER
8/15
"THE FASTEST, WILDEST, TWISTIEST, TURNIEST, MOST STOMACH-CHURNING EXPERIENCE OF A LIFETIME"!
GUT BUSTER
IS THAT A CHALLENGE?
GUT BUSTER
© 2000 by NEA, Inc.
IT... IT'S A RIDE.
HE TAKES HIS AMUSEMENT SERIOUSLY.
GUT BUSTER
Peirce

HA! I DID IT! I RODE THE GUT BUSTER WITHOUT GETTING SICK!
UNLIKE YOU GUYS, I'M NO CHICKEN!
MM-MM! KIELBASA!
*CHOKE!*... 'SCUSE ME A SEC.... (gurk)
RRRETCH!!
I THOUGHT YOU HATED KIELBASA.
MORE TO THE POINT, HE DOES!

I'M CAPTURING THE ENTIRE COUNTY FAIR ON TAPE!
HEY, FRANCIS! OVER HERE!
GET A SHOT OF ME IN ACTION WITH THE "TEST YOUR STRENGTH" HAMMER!
8/17
WUMP!
bing!
© 2000 by NEA, Inc.
WANT ME TO ZOOM IN ON THE SPACE BETWEEN "PANTYWAIST" AND "URKEL"?
HEY, REWIND! **REWIND!** THAT WAS A PRACTICE SWING!
Peirce

MAGNAFISH
WHIZZZZZ
8/18
TONG!
TURNS OUT THE GUY RUNNING THE "MAGNA-FISH" BOOTH HAS A STEEL PLATE IN HIS HEAD.
© 2000 by NEA, Inc.
Peirce

WHAT IS WITH THIS STUPID RIFLE? I'M AIMING RIGHT AT THE DUCKS AND NOTHING'S HAPPENING!
DANG! DANG!
POP! POP!
8/19
COME ON, YOU DUMB DUCKS! GO DOWN, WILL YOU!! *SPUTTER!* GO DOWN!! COME ON!!
POP! POP! POP!
YAAAH!!
SITTI DUC
GUNS DON'T KILL DUCKS, PEOPLE KILL DUCKS.
IN THIS CASE, ANYWAY.
AAAHH
Peirce

GORDIE! WHAT'S WITH THE BIG MESS!?
INVENTORY! I'VE GOT TO ACCOUNT FOR EVERY ITEM
IN THE STORE!
WHA-?... HEY, WHAT'S **THIS** DOING IN A **GARBAGE CAN**?
HM?... OH, WE'RE THROWING THAT OUT. YOU CAN TAKE IT IF YOU WANT.
REALLY?
IT'S ALL YOURS.
TEDDY!
CHECK OUT WHAT THEY WERE THROWING AWAY AT "KLASSIC KOMIX"!
WOW! CAPTAIN PICARD! HOW'D YOU-?
KRAK!
BIFF!
"HEADS UP"!
ALAS, POOR JEAN-LUC.

WHAT ARE WE DOING IN THIS NEIGHBORHOOD?
I JUST WANTED TO SHOW YOU THIS.
SHOW ME THIS? THIS IS MRS. GODFREY'S HOUSE! SO WHAT?
LOOK
SOLD
HOME & HEARTH REALTORS
CALL 555·7700
!
8/31
© 2000 by NEA, Inc.
SOLD! SOLD! SOLD!
I KNOW! I KNOW!
Peirce

I CAN'T BELIEVE IT! MRS. GODFREY IS MOVING!
WE'LL NEVER HAVE TO LOOK AT HER UGLY FACE AGAIN! BUT... WAIT!
WE... WE NEVER HAD A CHANCE TO SAY GOODBYE!
9/1
WA HA HA HA HA HA HA HA HA HA
OH HO HO HO HO
© 2000 by NEA, Inc.
I CRACK ME UP!
HERE, GET A PICTURE OF ME WITH THIS!
SOL

FRANCIS! WE JUST SAW A "SOLD" SIGN IN FRONT OF MRS. GODFREY'S HOUSE! SHE'S MOVING AWAY!
SHE'S NOT GOING TO BE OUR TEACHER ANYMORE! CAN YOU BELIEVE IT?
BUT... WHY IS THAT GOOD?
9/2
I MEAN... SHE MAY BE KIND OF TOUGH, BUT MRS. GODFREY'S A GOOD TEACHER! I'VE LEARNED A LOT FROM HER!
HE'S NEVER BEEN ONE OF US.
WEDGIE TIME.
HEY!
PEIRCE

TAPPA
TAPPA
TAPPA
TAPPITY
TAPPITY
TAPPA
9/4
SO LONG, DAD! I'M OFF TO SCHOOL! WANT ME TO SAY HI TO MRS. GODFREY FOR YOU?
TAPPA
TAPPA
TAPPITY
TAPPITY
OH WAIT, I FORGOT! MRS. GODFREY WON'T BE THERE BECAUSE... SHE MOVED!
WAHOOOO
TAPPA TAPPA
TAPPITY
TAPPA
Peirce

AH! WHAT A FEELING TO WALK INTO THE SCHOOL KNOWING THAT MRS. GODFREY HAS **MOVED AWAY**!
HELLO, SCHOOL! HELLO, YOU GREAT BIG BEAUTIFUL PILE OF BRICKS! I AM **SO HAPPY** TO SEE YOU!
MMMMMMM
SMAK! SMAK!
SMAK!
I'M GIDDY!
THANK YOU FOR POINTING THAT OUT.
© 2000 by NEA, Inc.
9/5
Peirce

HELLO THERE, NATE!
MISS CLARKE! HI! HOW ARE YOU? ISN'T IT A **GREAT** DAY?
GOODNESS! WHAT'S GOT **YOU** IN SUCH A GOOD MOOD?
AH! AS IF YOU DIDN'T KNOW!
WINKA WINK!
9/6
DOESN'T THE SCHOOL SEEM LIKE A HAPPIER, JOLLIER PLACE ALL OF A SUDDEN? IT'S LIKE A BLACK CLOUD HAS LIFTED! I MEAN... DING DONG, THE WITCH IS **DEAD**, AM I RIGHT?
NATE, YOU'RE MAKING EVEN LESS SENSE THAN YOU USUALLY DO.
WILL THERE BE A ROCKIN' TOGA PARTY IN THE TEACHERS' LOUNGE?
Peirce

THIS IS THE FIRST DAY OF THE REST OF OUR LIVES, TEDDY! THE GODFREY ERA IS OVER! IT'S OVER! IT'S OVER!
HELLO, BOYS.
!
MRS. GODFREY
9/7
WHA-? WHA-WHA-?... YOU... Y-YOU... CHOKE!
SIT DOWN, PLEASE.
IT'S OVER.
NO!
Peirce

M-MRS. GODFREY! WH-WHAT ARE YOU DOING HERE?
WHY **WOULDN'T** I BE HERE?
MRS. GODFREY
9/8
WE... WE SAW A "SOLD" SIGN IN FRONT OF YOUR HOUSE! WE THOUGHT YOU MOVED AWAY!
OH, WE **DID** MOVE!
WE MOVED INTO THE HOUSE ACROSS THE STREET! IT HAS TWO EXTRA ROOMS AND A BIGGER YARD!
MRS. GODFREY
JUST TO SPITE ME, THE WOMAN MOVES FIFTY FEET.
Peirce

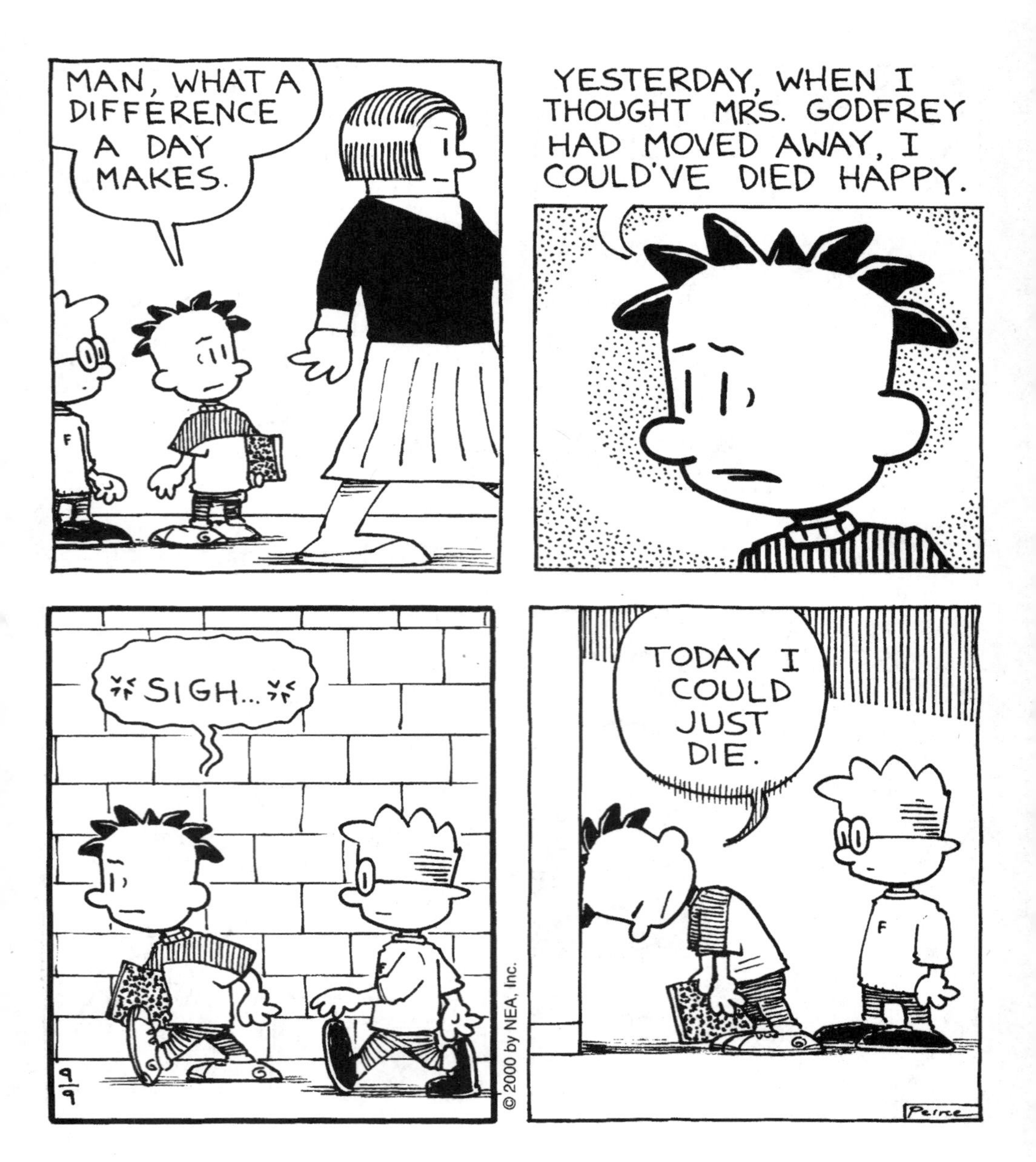
MAN, WHAT A DIFFERENCE A DAY MAKES.
YESTERDAY, WHEN I THOUGHT MRS. GODFREY HAD MOVED AWAY, I COULD'VE DIED HAPPY.
SIGH...
TODAY I COULD JUST DIE.
9/9
© 2000 by NEA, Inc.
Peirce

I'M CALLING THIS PAINTING "WHITE DOVE"!
IT LOOKS MORE LIKE A DUCK.
YEAH. HOW ABOUT "WHITE DUCK"?
SHUT UP, WILL YOU? YOU'RE BREAK-ING MY CONCEN- ...DANG!
"WHITE PIG"!
"WHITE ELEPHANT"!
GO AWAY!
© 2000 by NEA, Inc.

OKAY, GUYS, LET'S REHEARSE!
MUST WE?
EXCUSE ME, BUT CAN WE HAVE A LITTLE ENTHUSIASM HERE? WE'RE NEVER GOING TO ROCKET TO THE TOP OF THE CHARTS WITH THAT ATTITUDE!
10/5
NOW!... I'LL SING WHILE YOU GUYS DO SOME DANCE MOVES! TRY NOT TO SCREW IT UP!
...AND A-ONE AND A-TWO!... OOOOOH
IS A WEDGIE CONSIDERED A DANCE MOVE?
F
F
© 2000 by NEA, Inc.

WHICH MEMBER OF THE CONTINENTAL CONGRESS WAS THE...
OOH!
RICHARD HENRY LEE?
VERY GOOD, GINA! YOU ANTICIPATED MY QUESTION!
AND WHICH DELEGATE WAS SELECTED TO...
OOH!
THOMAS JEFFERSON?
DO YOU MIND, NATE? I WASN'T FINISHED! DON'T INTERRUPT ME AGAIN!
10/25
© 2000 by NEA, Inc.
THOMAS JEFFERSON?
VERY GOOD, GINA!
SIGH...

I STILL CAN'T BELIEVE MY DAD IS HANDING OUT **RICE CAKES** FOR HALLOWEEN!
HEY, TEDDY! WHAT'S IN THE BAG?
10 30
OOOOOH! **EGGS!**
YUP! AN EVEN DOZEN!
WHICH HOUSE SHALL WE TARGET FIRST?
THAT YELLOW ONE RIGHT THERE.
© 2000 by NEA, Inc.
YOU WANT TO EGG YOUR **OWN HOUSE**?
YOU MUST HAVE MISSED THE EARLIER RICE CAKE REFERENCE.
Peirce

I'M SERIOUS ABOUT THIS, FRANCIS. YOU'RE SPENDING WAY TOO MUCH TIME STUDYING!
THE QUESTION IS: WHY? YOU COULD PROBABLY GET STRAIGHT A'S WITHOUT STUDYING! WHY DO YOU DO IT?
AND DON'T GIVE ME SOME CHEESY, PENCIL-NECK ANSWER LIKE...
BECAUSE I'M NOT CONTENT WITH MEDIOCRITY.
DID YOU NOT HEAR WHAT I JUST SAID?
...EXCEPT IN MY CHOICE OF BEST FRIENDS.
11/14
Peirce

THIS IS RIDICULOUS! HOW ARE WE SUPPOSED TO PLAY HOCKEY WITH MY SISTER AND HER FIGURE-SKATING PALS HACKING UP THE ICE?
...AND IT'S NOT LIKE THEY'RE ANY GOOD AT IT! I MEAN, IT'S NOT LIKE THEY'RE MICHELLE KWAN OUT THERE!
12/9
WHO'S MICHELLE KWAN?
© 2000 by NEA, Inc.
SHE'S A FIGURE SKATER, ISN'T SHE?
DO YOU WATCH FIGURE SKATING?!
BIG MISTAKE.
Peirce

HEY, DID YOU HEAR ABOUT OUR "HARRY POTTER" CLUB? TEDDY IS RON... SHEILA IS HERMIONE... AND I'M HARRY!
7TH G
BAK
SAL
HOW COME **YOU** GET TO BE HARRY? **I** WANT TO BE HARRY!
SORRY, I GOT DIBS ON HARRY. YOU CAN BE NEVILLE.
1/17
**NEVILLE??** BUT HE'S A TOTAL **SCREWUP!**
EXACTLY!
WILL NATE WRIGHT REPORT TO THE DETENTION ROOM?
HEY, YOUR FLY'S OPEN.
YOU'RE **PER-FECT** FOR HIM!
Peirce

HI, BUTTHEAD!
HI, UGLY!
HI, PIZZA FACE!
HI, PENCIL NECK!
HI, FISH BREATH!
HI, PEA BRAIN!
HA HA HA HA HA HA HA
HI, GEEK BOY!
HELLO, CLUELESS!
HA HA HA HA HA HA HA HA
HI, BANANA NOSE!
HI, SQUIRREL TEETH!
HA HA HA HA HA
HELLO, BOYS.
HI, FATSO!
DETENTION
HI STUPID
Peirce

DANG! I CAN'T THINK OF WHAT TO DRAW. GIVE ME AN IDEA.
P.S. 38 CARTOONI CLUB
3/23
UM... MRS. GODFREY.
MORE. I NEED MORE.
P.S. 38 CARTOON CLUB
MRS. GODFREY IN THE HOSPITAL.
MORE. MORE.
MRS. GODFREY IN THE HOSPITAL AFTER A HORRIBLY BOTCHED LIPOSUCTION PROCEDURE!
HIGH FIVE ME!
Peirce

YOU'LL NOTICE, BOYS, THAT I'VE GOT MY TRUSTY NOTEPAD!
A GREAT CARTOONIST ALWAYS TAKES HIS NOTEPAD WHEREVER HE GOES!
THAT WAY, IF I SEE SOMETHING HILARIOUS HAPPENING, I CAN DRAW IT RIGHT AWAY! ON THE SPOT!
4/1
OOH! I SEE SOMETHING HILARIOUS! RIGHT THERE!
WHERE?
SSSLIP!
PLOOSH
SCRIBBLE SCRIBBLE SCRIBBLE
APRIL FOOL!
DUH.
Peirce

NATE'S GOING ALL OVER THE SCHOOL TRYING TO FIND A GIRL HE CAN TAKE TO MEGAN'S PARTY!
I KNOW.
HE'S TOTALLY DESPERATE!
OH, I DON'T KNOW IF I'D USE THE WORD "DESPERATE"...
ATTENTION, LADIES! LOOKING FOR A DATE TO MEGAN'S PARTY? **NATE WRIGHT** IS YOUR MAN!
4/3
© 2001 by NEA, Inc.
I'M 4'6", 87 POUNDS, A SCORPIO...
GET OFF THE INTERCOM, NATE.
I WAS GOING TO SAY "PATHETIC."
Peirce

HEY, LOOK! THE SPRING PLAY IS GONNA BE "PETER PAN"!
OOH! I'M TRYING OUT FOR THAT!
4/16
YOU?
YOU?
WHAT'S THAT SUPPOSED TO MEAN?
YOU CAN'T ACT, THAT'S WHAT!
YEAH, REMEMBER WHEN YOU WERE SNOOPY IN "YOU'RE A GOOD MAN, CHARLIE BROWN"?
© 2001 by NEA, Inc.
HEY, FALLING OFF A DOGHOUSE CAN HAPPEN TO ANYONE!
FIVE TIMES?
WE HAD TO IMPROVISE THAT SNOOPY WAS DISORIENTED FROM HIS TAPEWORM MEDICATION!
Peirce

EVERYONE, THIS IS ARTUR. HE'S JUST MOVED TO THIS COUNTRY AND WANTS TO JOIN OUR CHESS TEAM!
PLAY CHESS
HEY, ARTUR! I'M NATE! I'M OUR TEAM'S NUMBER ONE PLAYER! I'D BE HAPPY TO TAKE YOU UNDER MY WING, SHOW YOU A FEW MOVES, THAT SORT OF THING!
HELLO
5/7
ARTUR WAS THE BOYS' AGE-GROUP CHESS CHAMPION OF BELARUS!
© 2001 by NEA, Inc.
BELARUS?
VERY SMALL COUNTRY. BARELY ELEVEN MILLION.
Peirce

EVERYBODY KNOWS DOGS ARE BETTER THAN CATS.
WE'RE NOT GOING TO HAVE THIS ARGUMENT AGAIN, ARE WE?
HOT DOG!
COOL CAT!
PUTTIN' ON THE DOG!
IN THE CATBIRD SEAT!
HOW MUCH IS THAT DOGGY IN THE WINDOW...
OH THE CAT'S IN THE CRADLE AND THE SILVER SPOON...
DOG FIGHT!
CAT BURGLAR!
DOG TAGS!
CATTAILS!
DOG PADDLE!
CATWALK!
LOOK, CAN WE STOP THIS NONSENSE?
5/20
OKAY, SURE. I COULD USE A BREAK...
... BECAUSE I'M DOG TIRED!!
SO TAKE A CAT-NAP.

MUST YOU KEEP DOING THAT?
bounce bounce bounce bounce bounce bounce bounce
DOING WHAT?
BOUNCING YOUR LEG LIKE THAT! YOU'RE MAKING THE WHOLE FLOOR SHAKE! IT'S REALLY, REALLY ANNOYING ME!
I DIDN'T KNOW THAT.
WELL, NOW YOU KNOW!
6/4
© 2001 by NEA, Inc.
bounce bounce bounce bounce bounce bounce bounce bounce
Peirce

I KNOW THIS STUFF COLD! HERE! QUIZ ME!
OKAY
1785.
1785?
UM... WAS THAT SHAYS' REBELLION?
NOPE.
HMMM... I WAS SURE I KNEW ALL THESE. UH.... THE NORTHWEST ORDINANCE?
NO.
THE CONSTITUTIONAL CONVENTION?... THE WHISKEY REBELLION?
SORRY
THE COINAGE ACT?... THE NATURALIZATION ACT?... THE FIRST CONGRESS?... THE BILL OF RIGHTS??
NOPE
WELL, WHAT IS IT??
IT'S THE SERIAL NUMBER ON THE BACK OF THIS TEXTBOOK!
WA HA HA HA HA HA OH HO HO HO
THIS MUST BE WHY THEY CALL IT "CRAMMING."
Peirce

I CAN'T BELIEVE YOU! ARTUR TAKES YOUR PLACE AS OUR BEST PLAYER, AND SO YOU'RE QUITTING THE TEAM?
YOU DON'T UNDERSTAND.
I DON'T UNDERSTAND? GEE, WHY WOULD I UNDERSTAND? THE EXACT SAME THING ONLY HAPPENED TO ME!
WHAT ARE YOU TALKING ABOUT?
9/26
NATE, BEFORE YOU JOINED THE TEAM, I WAS OUR NUMBER ONE PLAYER!
BUT THAT WAS DIFFERENT! I WAS SO CLEARLY BETTER THAN YOU!
© 2001 by NEA, Inc.
IS THERE NO END TO YOUR SELF-ABSORPTION?
PLUS, I'M SO MUCH MORE LOVABLE THAN ARTUR!
Peirce

BLATT! HONK! SQUORK!
WHOA! STOP! WHAT ARE YOU DOING?
REHEARSING! I'VE COMPOSED A LOVE SONG FOR KELLY! I WANT TO RECORD IT AND SEND IT TO HER IN THE MAIL!
WILL YOU TAPE ME?
10/9
© 2001 by NEA, Inc.
Peirce

ARTISTS COME IN FOUR DIFFERENT CATEGORIES: STARVING, SELF-DESTRUCTIVE, BROODING, AND INSANE.
10/17
© 2001 by NEA, Inc.
LET ME GUESS: INSANE?
NO, BROODING! BROOD-ING!!
PEIRCE

TRICK OR TREAT!
HI, FRANCIS! HI, TEDDY! NATE'LL BE RIGHT DOWN!
WHILE YOU WAIT, WOULD YOU LIKE A **HOMEMADE** CRISPY FUDGE TREAT?
10/31
ER... THAT'S OKAY.
DON'T WANT TO RUIN MY APPETITE.
DO US A FAVOR, DAD. TURN OFF THE PORCH LIGHT AND CLOSE THE DRAPES.
Peirce

HEY, GUYS! WHAT'S UP?
NOT MUCH. JUST GETTING READY FOR THE MATH TEST.
WHAT MATH TEST?
THE MATH TEST NEXT PERIOD.
THERE'S A **MATH TEST** NEXT PERIOD??
IT SAYS SO RIGHT ON OUR STUDY GUIDE: "TEST WEDNESDAY."
TODAY'S WEDNES-DAY??
SHALL I HIT HIM WITH MY NOTE-BOOK?
NO, USE THIS. IT'S HARDCOVER.
© 2001 by NEA, Inc.
11/28
Peirce

... SO THEN THE DUCK SAYS, "JUST BILL ME!"
UH.....
I DON'T GET IT.
I KNOW THAT JOKE. DUCK IS SUPPOSED TO BE SAYING, "JUST PUT IT ON MY BILL."
WA HA HA HA HA
HA HA HA HA H
HA HA HA HA H
NOW THAT'S FUNNY!
GOOD ONE, ARTUR!
THIS KID'S STARTING TO BUG ME.
12/4
Peirce

HEY, ARTUR! WANT TO JOIN THE CARTOONING CLUB?
I DO NOT KNOW. AT DRAWING, I AM NOT SO GOOD.
12/5
OH, COME ON! GIVE IT A TRY! IT'S FUN!
WELL, HOKAY. I WILL DRAW OLD-FASHIONED AUTOMOBILE.
WOW!
WITH RULER AND COMPASS, I COULD DO BETTER.
I CAN'T TAKE IT.
Peirce

HIKE!
WHOA! TIME OUT!
LOOK! THE FIRST SNOW-FLAKE OF THE YEAR! EVERY-BODY MAKE A WISH!
MAKE A WISH? ON A SNOW-FLAKE?
SURE! WHY NOT?
12/16
YOU DON'T WISH ON A SNOWFLAKE, YOU IDIOT! YOU WISH ON A STAR!
WHO SAYS?
EVERYBODY SAYS! EVERYBODY KNOWS THAT YOU MAKE A WISH ON THE FIRST STAR!
WOMP!
LOOK AT THEM ALL.
GOT MY WISH!
Peirce

GUYS! READY FOR OUR ANNUAL NEW YEAR'S EVE MONOPOLY GAME?
OH, YEAH!
ABSO-LUTELY!
12/31
!! ARTUR!
HALLO, NATE. FRANCIS INVITED FOR ME TO PLAY IN YOUR GAME.
HE DID! WELL! THAT'S FRANCIS, ALL RIGHT! INVITING YOU TO JOIN OUR LITTLE GAME!
PAT
PAT
Peirce
© 2001 by NEA, Inc.
OUR LITTLE GAME!... OUR LITTLE GAME!
OW!
WHAP!
WHAP!
WHAP!
WHAP!

YOU OWE ME 1400 BUCKS, NATE! PAY UP!
HAH! YOU'RE BANKRUPT!
AU CONTRAIRE, MY FRIENDS!
ONE HUNDRED... TWO HUNDRED... THREE..
LOOK AT THAT WAD! YOU'VE BEEN STEALING FROM THE BANK!
I HAVE NOT! I'VE BEEN KEEPING A SECRET STASH HIDDEN IN MY UNDERWEAR!
1-4-02
© 2001 by NEA, Inc.
FOUR HUNDRED... FIVE HUNDRED...
OKAY, TIME OUT FOR A LYSOL BREAK.
Peirce

WELL! I LANDED ON ILLINOIS AVENUE! I'M BUSTED! LOOKS LIKE YOU WIN, ARTUR!
NOT TOO SHABBY FOR YOUR FIRST GAME OF MONOPOLY **EVER**! YOU WIPED US ALL OUT!
1/5/02
SO LONG, ARTUR! GREAT GAME! SEE YOU MONDAY! THANKS FOR COMING!
OH, HOW I HATE HIM.
Peirce

OKAY, SPITSY, HERE'S THE PLAN:
FRANCIS AND TEDDY ARE OVER AT THE PLAYGROUND.
12/30
YOU LURE THEM OVER HERE SO I CAN AMBUSH THEM WITH A SNOWBALL BARRAGE! OKAY? GO!
WOOF! WOOF! BARK! ARF!
HEY, IT'S SPITSY!
WOOF WOOF
HE'S FREAKING OUT!
WHAT IS IT, SPITSY? WHAT'S WRONG?
WOOF!
ROWF!
I THINK HE WANTS US TO FOLLOW HIM!
MAYBE SOMEBODY'S IN TROUBLE! LET'S GO!
WHERE ARE THEY? COME ON, SPITSY!
IT SHOULDN'T TAKE THIS LONG TO GET TO THE PLAYGROUND AND B-...
...-ACK.
BAD, BAD, BAD, BAD, BAD, BAD, BAD, BAD, BAD, BAD, BAD, BAD DOG.
Peirce

IF YOU'RE SICK OF GINA ANSWERING EVERY QUESTION IN CLASS, WHY DON'T YOU RAISE YOUR HAND?
I'VE TRIED! IT'S NO USE!
GINA BEATS EVERYONE TO THE PUNCH! THE SECOND A QUESTION IS ASKED, HER HAND SHOOTS INTO THE AIR LIKE A BOTTLE ROCKET!
1/26
SHE'S LIKE AN ANIMAL! SHE'S A CRAZED GREYHOUND GOING AFTER A MECHANICAL RABBIT AT WARP SPEED!
© 2002 by NEA, Inc.
HER "FAST-TWITCH" MUSCLES MAKE HER SO QUICK!
QUICKER THAN YOU KNOW.
Peirce

"SIXTH-GRADE BAKE SALE WEDNESDAY"... PLAIN BLACK BLOCK LETTERS... BORING!
A POSTER IS SUPPOSED TO BE EYE-CATCHING! IT NEEDS TO JUMP OFF THE WALL! THIS ONE JUST SITS THERE!
2/5
SOME PEOPLE JUST DON'T KNOW WHAT TO DO WITH A PAINTBRUSH IN THEIR HANDS!
Peirce

HEY, FRANCIS! WANNA PLAY SNOW FOOTBALL!?
SURE!
BUT WHERE'S THE FOOTBALL?
I'LL SHOW YOU!
2/10
WHEN I SAY "SNOW FOOTBALL"...
PAT PAT
... I MEAN **SNOW** FOOTBALL!
HEE HEE! COOL!
GO LONG!
HEAVE!
WHOMP!
INTERCEPTION!!
YOU ARE **SO** DEAD.
Peirce

HEADS UP!
HUH?
OW!
BONK!
THANKS A LOT, FRANCIS!
HEY, I SAID HEADS UP!
EXACTLY! YOU SAID HEADS UP! SO I LOOKED UP!
SO?
SO IT WAS A GROUND BALL, FOOL!
WELL, WHAT AM I SUPPOSED TO SAY? "HEADS DOWN"?
SAY ANYTHING! ANYTHING THAT MAKES SENSE!
HOW ABOUT THIS: LOOK OUT!
4/14
GOOD! MUCH BETTER!
LOOK OUT! LOOK OUT!
LOOK OUT!
OKAY, FRANCIS! YOU'VE MADE YOUR POINT! YOU DON'T HAVE TO...
peirce

THUNK THUNK THUNK THUNK THUNK THUNK
WHAT ON EARTH ARE YOU DOING?
I'M HITTING MYSELF IN THE HEAD WITH AN EMPTY TWO-LITER PLASTIC SODA BOTTLE.
THUNK THUNK THUNK THUNK THUNK THUNK
DUH.
"DUH" WAS GOING TO BE **MY** LINE.
DON'T TRY TO PRETEND LIKE YOU HAVEN'T DONE IT.
THUNK THUNK UNK UNK HUNK THUNK THUNK
7/29
Peirce
© 2002 by NEA, Inc.

I'M BECOMING A MASTER BLUESMAN.
8/6
DON'T YOU HAVE TO **SUFFER** TO PLAY THE BLUES?
OH, I'VE SUFFERED PLENTY, MY FRIEND.
I LOST ONE OF MY LUCKY SOCKS, WE'RE HAVING TUNA CASSEROLE FOR SUPPER, AND MY DAD WON'T LET ME GET A GAMEBOY.
CATCHY LYRICS.
PLUS, I'M A RED SOX FAN.
Peirce

MY CAR IS CALLED "THUNDER"!
MINE'S "THE BEAST"!
I CALL MINE "BLOOD SPORT"!
COOL PAINT JOB!
THAT'S NOT PAINT!
8/22
DERBY
GROSS.
MY DAD WAS HELPING ME, AND HE CUT HIS FINGER!
© 2002 by NEA, Inc.
Peirce

SNACK BAR?
SNACK BAR!
I'M STARVING!
OKAY, I'VE GOT... HMM... I'VE GOT $3.55...
A HOT DOG IS $1.75... A SODA IS 85 CENTS... ICE CREAM IS $1.20...
DO I HAVE ENOUGH TO BUY ALL THREE? LET'S SEE HERE...
$1.75 PLUS .85... THAT'S... UH... THAT'S $2.60... PLUS... UMMM...
WAIT A MINUTE! WHAT AM I DOING?
WHAT ARE YOU DOING?
MATH! I'M DOING MATH!
I'M DOING MATH! DURING SUMMER VACATION!!
8/25
THIS IS WRONG! THIS IS SO WRONG!
HERE. YOU FIGURE IT OUT.
HE'S A MAN OF PRINCIPLE.
Peirce

June's the month we made our break,
To spend our days at beach and lake.
July and August: play, play, play.
Weren't we here just yesterday?
P.S. 38
MIDDLE SCH
WELCOME
BACK!
© 2002 by NEA, Inc.
Peirce

*SNIFF!* YOUR FEET **REEK!**
MY FEET? WHAT ABOUT **YOUR BREATH**, GINA?
YOU CAN SMELL FROM ACROSS THE **ROOM** WHAT YOU HAD FOR LUNCH! TUNA FISH, NACHO CHEESE DORITOS, BANANA YOGURT, AND ORANGE SODA!
9/10
THAT'S WHAT **YOU** HAD FOR LUNCH.
OH.
HAVE A CERTS.
PLEASE.

WHAT'S UP WITH YOU AND GINA, NATE?
YEAH! ALL YOU TWO DO IS ARGUE ALL THE TIME!
HEY, YOU WOULD TOO IF SHE SAT NEXT TO YOU! SHE THINKS SHE'S SO GREAT, BUT MAN!... SHE IS JUST TOTALLY OBNOXIOUS!
9/12
NATE AND GINA HAVE A "LOVE-HATE" THING GOING ON!
EXACTLY! SHE'S COM-PLETELY...
© 2002 by NEA, Inc.
!... NO!! NOT "LOVE-HATE"!! JUST HATE! IT'S ALL HATE!
OOOOOOOH!
Peirce

I WONDER WHY MRS. GODFREY HATES ME SO MUCH.
HEY! WHY DON'T WE THINK OF ALL THE THINGS WE HATE ABOUT YOU, AND CROSS-REFERENCE THEM WITH STUFF SHE MIGHT DESPISE!
GOOD IDEA!

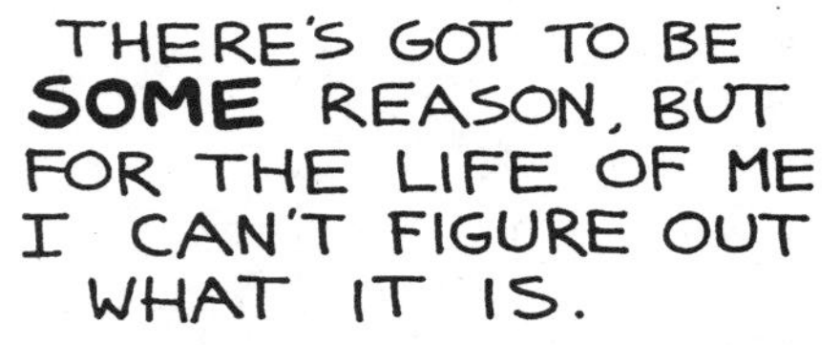
THERE'S GOT TO BE SOME REASON, BUT FOR THE LIFE OF ME I CAN'T FIGURE OUT WHAT IT IS.

9/25

WELL, THERE'S HIS VOICE!
IT'S SO NASAL!
sigh...
Peirce

WE HAVE TO WRITE A HAIKU FOR ENGLISH CLASS!
WHAT'S A HAIKU?
JAPANESE POETRY!
IT'S SUPPOSED TO HAVE SEVENTEEN SYLLABLES!
ALLOW ME TO DEMON-STRATE, TEDDY!
10/7
"YOU HAVE CHEEZ DOODLES. ORANGE, DELICIOUS, CRUNCHY. GIVE ME ONE RIGHT NOW."
THIS MAY BE THE FIRST TIME A HAIKU HAS BEEN USED TO MOOCH JUNK FOOD.
YOU DIDN'T SAY "PLEASE".
THAT'D BE TOO MANY SYLLABLES.
NARF
NARF NARF
Peirce

HEY, DID YOU HEAR? CURTIS'S ANKLE IS BROKEN!
DANG!
WE'VE LOST THREE PLAYERS IN A WEEK!
I KNOW. COACH WANTS US TO RECRUIT A COUPLE KIDS TO FILL IN!
HEY! HOW ABOUT ARTUR?
NO!
10/15
NO! NOT ARTUR! DEFINITELY NOT ARTUR! ANYBODY BUT ARTUR!
© 2002 by NEA, Inc.
ARTUR IT IS!
LET'S GO ASK HIM!
I GET NO RESPECT.
Peirce

NATE!
HUH?
10/20
HAVE YOU EVER HEARD OF A LITTLE SOMETHING CALLED BODY LANGUAGE?
UH... I GUESS SO.
WELL, YOURS IS AWFUL! YOU'RE SLOUCHING! YOU'RE ALL SLUMPED OVER!
A STUDENT IN MY CLASS NEEDS TO LOOK ALERT! YOU NEED TO SHOW ME YOU'RE READY TO LEARN!
PSST! NATE! I CAN HELP YOU WITH THAT!
HMM?
YANK!
NOW THAT'S MORE LIKE IT!
BEHOLD THE POWER OF THE WEDGIE.
PEIRCE

NATE "SCOOP" WRIGHT AT YOUR SERVICE, CITIZENS! I'M GATHERING TIDBITS FOR "CLASSROOM CHATTER"!
YOUR GOSSIP COLUMN?
PARDON **MOI**, TEDDY, BUT IT IS **NOT** A "GOSSIP COLUMN"! I AM A **JOURNALIST**, NOT A PURVEYOR OF **RUMOR** AND **INNUENDO**!
OH. RIGHT.
11/18
NOW... ANY GOOD IDEAS FOR MY NEXT HEADLINE?
"REPORTER TAKES SELF TOO SERIOUSLY."
"**ALLEGED** REPORTER."
OOH, **YES!** WHO'S THE NIMROD?
Peirce

AH HA!
THERE'S FRANCIS! NOW REVENGE WILL BE MINE!
"REVENGE"?
2/23
HE NOOGIED ME THIS MORNING IN THE CAFETERIA!
I DON'T GET NOOGIES, I GIVE THEM! I'M THE NOOGIE KING!
EXCUSE ME, TEDDY, WHILE I PAY HIM BACK BIG TIME!
!
ZZZZOOOP!
CRASH!
I BUTTERED MY HEAD!
PRETTY SLICK!
Peirce

THIS IS AN OUTRAGE! WE CAN'T EVEN GET A BAG OF "CHEEZ DOODLES" IN OUR OWN CAFETERIA! THANK YOU, SCHOOL BOARD!
4/17
OH, WHAT A BETRAYAL OF ALL THAT IS SACRED AND HOLY!
HA HA HEE! LISTEN TO YOU!
YEAH, NATE! ISN'T "SACRED AND HOLY" A BIT DRAMATIC?
IT'S MORE LIKE A BETRAYAL OF ALL THAT IS CRUNCHY AND CHEESY!
NO! NO! A BETRAYAL OF ALL THAT IS ORANGE AND CURLY!
HA HA HA HA
HA HA HA HA HA HA
CURLY AND PUFFY!
CURLY AND LARRY!
HA HA HA HA HA HA HA HA HA HA HA HA
WHERE IS THE EMPATHY?
Peirce
© 2003 by NEA, Inc.

HEY, FRANCIS! WANNA TRADE? WHAT DO YOU HAVE?
TOFU BAR.
4 19
TEDDY! WHAT'VE YOU GOT THERE?
RICE CAKE.
SHEILA! GOT ANYTHING GOOD?
BRAN MUFFIN.
STOCKING THE SNACK MACHINE WITH HEALTH FOOD HAS TAKEN ALL THE JOY OUT OF THE LUNCHTIME BARTER SYSTEM.
Peirce

OOOOH! CHECK THIS OUT! A TALENT SHOW!
WITH AWESOME PRIZES!
FINALLY, MY CHANCE FOR STARDOM! I CAN'T WAIT TO GET UP ON STAGE!
YOU? WHAT CAN YOU DO?
AHEM!... I BELIEVE THE QUESTION, TEDDY, IS: WHAT CAN'T I DO?
SHALL WE START A LIST?
LET'S ALPHABETIZE IT!
SHUT UP.
Peirce

GREETINGS, TALENT LOVERS!
HA HA HA HEE HEE
WHAT ARE YOU SUP-POSED TO BE, A VAMPIRE?
NO, YOU IDIOT, I'M A MAGICIAN! I DECIDED TO DO A MAGIC PERFORMANCE IN THE TALENT SHOW!
I THOUGHT YOU WERE GOING TO DO COMEDY!
4 28
CHANGED MY MIND! WHY MAKE PEOPLE LAUGH WHEN I CAN DAZZLE THEM?
OOPS.
IN YOUR CASE, YOU CAN DO BOTH!
Peirce

HEY, WE'VE GOT A FILMSTRIP IN SOCIAL STUDIES! HIGH FIVE!
NOPE. NO MORE HIGH FIVES.
HIGH FIVES ARE SO **PAST** IT, YOU KNOW? THAT SHIP HAS **SAILED!** IT'S TIME TO INVENT A **NEW** KIND OF HIGH FIVE!
5/12
HOW 'BOUT A **MEDIUM** FIVE? NOT UP HIGH, NOT DOWN LOW!
LIKE THIS, YOU MEAN?
PAT PAT
HEY! LOOKIT THE WUSSY-BOYS PLAYING PATTY-CAKE!!
BAD IDEA.
Peirce

HOW 'BOUT THIS: WE BUMP OUR FISTS TOGETHER!
NAH. THAT'S BEEN AROUND FOR YEARS.
DANG! HOW ARE WE GONNA COME UP WITH A NEW VARIATION ON THE HIGH FIVE? EVERYTHING'S BEEN DONE ALREADY!
5/13
LET'S DO A LOW FIVE! WE TOUCH THE FLOOR, THEN SLAP HANDS!
OKAY, LET'S TRY IT.
NURSE
F
PEIRCE

WE MAKE A "PEACE" SIGN, THEN SLAP FINGERS DOWN LOW!
I LIKE IT!

WE DID IT! WE REINVENTED THE HIGH FIVE!
HIGH FIVE ME!

5/17

WAIT A MINUTE.
IRONY ALERT.

HUH?? I ONLY GOT A 94 ON THE TEST!
OH, NO, GINA! SAY IT ISN'T SO!
I CAN'T THINK OF ANYTHING MORE DEVASTATING FOR YOU THAN TO GET A 94 ON A TEST!
6/2
© 2003 by NEA, Inc.
EXCEPT...
A 96?!
Peirce

HOW COULD YOU HAVE GOTTEN A 96?? LEMME SEE THAT!
READ IT AND WEEP, M'LADY!
WAIT A MINUTE! SHE MISSED A QUESTION THAT YOU GOT WRONG! A TEN-POINTER!
6/3
THIS SHOULD BE AN 86, NOT A 96!
AH, WELL! SO BE IT!
MRS. GODFREY!
WHOA! WHOA!
Peirce

MRS. GODFREY! I WAS JUST LOOKING AT NATE'S TEST, AND...
AT **NATE'S** TEST?
GODFREY
6/4
YES! AND **LOOK**! YOU MISSED THIS QUESTION THAT HE GOT **WRONG**! THAT'S A TEN-POINT MISTAKE!
HE GOT A **96** WHEN HE ONLY DESERVED AN **86**!
MRS. GODFREY
NATE? COME UP HERE TO MY DESK, PLEASE.
OH, HOW I HATE HER.
Peirce

NATE, GINA HAS POINTED OUT THAT I MADE A MISTAKE WHEN I GRADED YOUR TEST.
SHE CONTENDED THAT I SHOULD HAVE GIVEN YOU AN 86, NOT A 96, AND SHE WAS RIGHT.
GINA, HOWEVER, DOES NOT TEACH THIS CLASS. I DO. NATE, YOU'LL KEEP YOUR 96.
YES!
GINA, WE'RE NOT DONE.
Peirce

FRANKLY, GINA, I'M APPALLED BY YOUR EFFORTS TO "CORRECT" NATE'S TEST SCORE.
B-BUT... HE GOT A GRADE HE DIDN'T DESERVE!
YES, I MADE A MISTAKE... BUT WHAT CONCERN IS THAT OF **YOURS**? FOR YOU TO POINT THAT OUT IS SPITEFUL AND MEAN-SPIRITED!
**NATE** SHOULDN'T BE PUNISHED FOR AN ERROR THAT **I** MADE... AND HE WON'T BE.
6/6
© 2003 by NEA, Inc.
**SOME**ONE, HOWEVER, **WILL** BE DISCIPLINED.
THIS IS THE HAPPIEST DAY OF MY LIFE!
Peirce

WHAT A DAY! WHAT A DAY! I GET A 96 ON THE TEST, AND GINA GETS DETENTION!
I NEVER THOUGHT MRS. GODFREY WOULD BRING THE HAMMER DOWN ON GINA! SHE ACTUALLY TOOK MY SIDE! SHE WAS ACTUALLY FAIR ABOUT IT!
I COULD HAVE KISSED HER!
OOOOOOH!
BUT THAT PASSED! IT PASSED!
© 2003 by NEA, Inc.

the COMPETITION
10 FT
CANNONBALL
JACKKNIFE
SWAN DIVE
FLIP
CORKSCREW
6/15
ZOOP!
WINNER
CLAP
CLAP CLAP
CLAP
CLAP CLAP
CLAP
CLAP CLAP
CLAP
CLAP CLAP
CLAP
Peirce

NEXT WEEK'S THE LAST DAY OF SCHOOL! I'VE GOTTA COME UP WITH A GOOD PRANK!
A PRANK?
YEAH! THE LAST DAY OF SCHOOL IS "PRANK DAY," FRANCIS! EVERYBODY KNOWS THAT!
"PRANK DAY"?
6/16
IT DOESN'T SAY ANYTHING ABOUT "PRANK DAY" IN **HERE**.
Peirce
HEY, **THERE'S** A SHOCKER! THEY DON'T MENTION "PRANK DAY" IN THE **STUDENT HANDBOOK**!
DUDE, YOU **HIGHLIGHTED** IT?

No talking loud;
No chewing gum;
No wearing caps in school.
For every human impulse,
There is bound to be
A rule.
TRASH
6/21
"No racing in
The hallways!"
Is a cry we often hear,
© 2003 by NEA, Inc.
But who would cut
The engine
With the finish line so near?
MATH
PEIRCE

AHHHH, SUMMER!! NO MORE HOMEWORK! NO MORE BOOKS!
YES! NO MORE BOOKS!
I'M NOT EVEN GOING TO THINK ABOUT READING A BOOK FOR THE NEXT TWO MONTHS!!
THE NEW "HARRY POTTER"!
!
© 2003 by NEA, Inc.
peirce

NATE! YOU ALMOST HIT ME WITH THAT FRISBEE!
SORRY, GINA, BUT THAT'S ONE OF THE HAZARDS OF BEING A SPECTATOR.
SPECTATOR? A SPECTATOR OF WHAT?
OUR FRISBEE GOLF TOURNAMENT!
YOUR WHAT? LOOK, I'M JUST TRYING TO READ!
THEN WHY ARE YOU SITTING IN THE MIDDLE OF THE TWELFTH FAIRWAY?
6/27
© 2003 by NEA, Inc.
I HATE PEOPLE WHO DON'T LIKE SPORTS.
Peirce

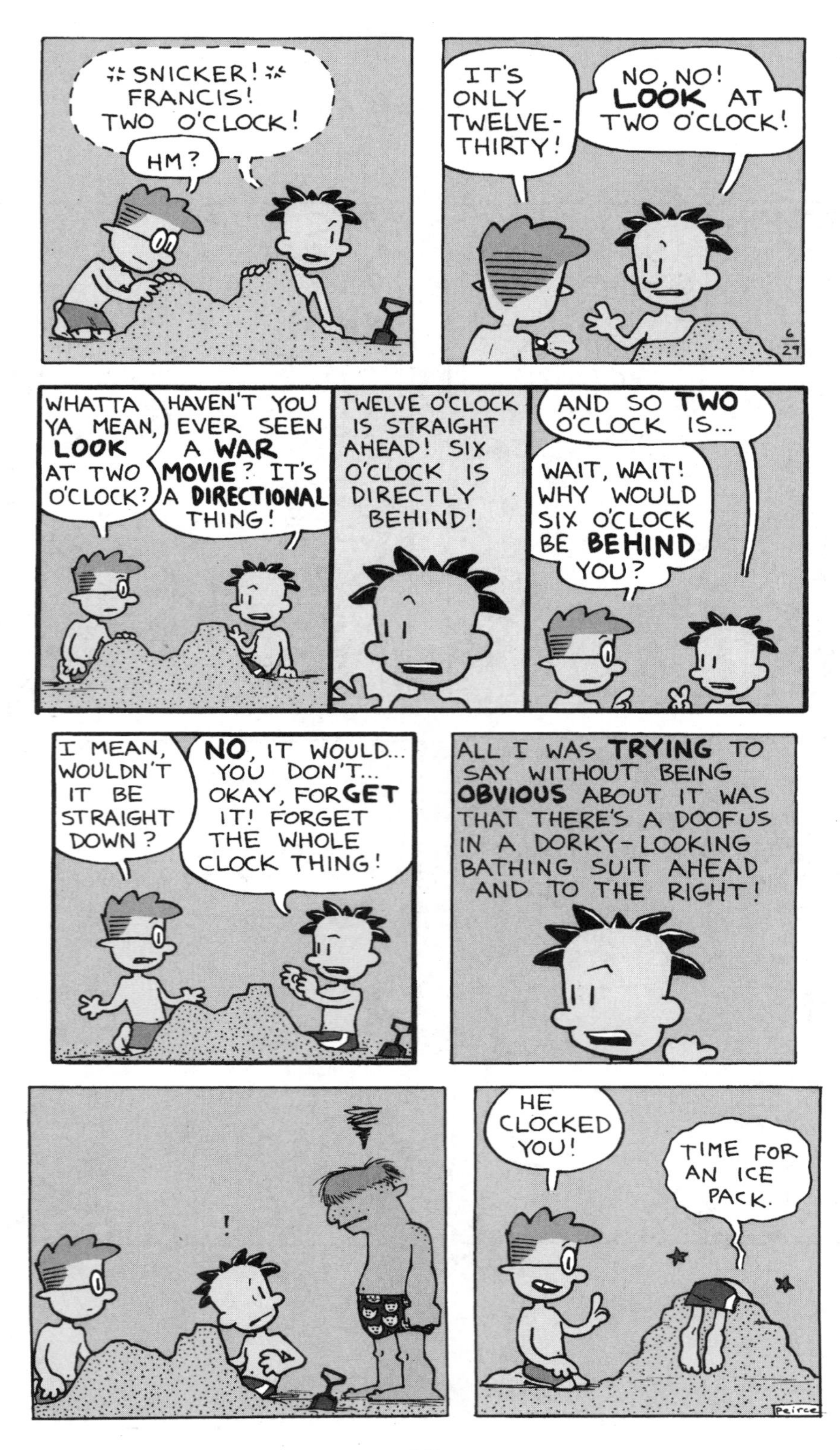

*SNICKER!* FRANCIS! TWO O'CLOCK!
HM?
IT'S ONLY TWELVE-THIRTY!
NO, NO! LOOK AT TWO O'CLOCK!
6/29
WHATTA YA MEAN, LOOK AT TWO O'CLOCK?
HAVEN'T YOU EVER SEEN A WAR MOVIE? IT'S A DIRECTIONAL THING!
TWELVE O'CLOCK IS STRAIGHT AHEAD! SIX O'CLOCK IS DIRECTLY BEHIND!
AND SO TWO O'CLOCK IS...
WAIT, WAIT! WHY WOULD SIX O'CLOCK BE BEHIND YOU?
I MEAN, WOULDN'T IT BE STRAIGHT DOWN?
NO, IT WOULD... YOU DON'T... OKAY, FORGET IT! FORGET THE WHOLE CLOCK THING!
ALL I WAS TRYING TO SAY WITHOUT BEING OBVIOUS ABOUT IT WAS THAT THERE'S A DOOFUS IN A DORKY-LOOKING BATHING SUIT AHEAD AND TO THE RIGHT!
!
HE CLOCKED YOU!
TIME FOR AN ICE PACK.
Peirce

WHAT DO YOU CALL A DWARF WITH ESP WHO ESCAPES FROM PRISON?
A SMALL MEDIUM AT LARGE!
8/14
OH HO HO HO H
WA HA HA HA H
HA HA HA
HA HA
THIS HEAT WAVE IS ROBBING PEOPLE OF THEIR ABILITY TO APPRECIATE COMEDIC GENIUS.
Peirce

HERE COMES MY PET PROJECT!
CHESTER?
CHESTER IS YOUR PET PROJECT?
THAT'S RIGHT! I'M GOING TO REFORM HIM!
REFORM HIM? WHY?
LOOK, EVERYONE'S AFRAID OF THE GUY, RIGHT?
...BUT HE MUST HAVE SOME GOOD IN HIM! NOBODY'S BORN THAT MEAN!
9/21
HE ACTS LIKE A BULLY BECAUSE NOBODY'S EVER BEEN NICE TO HIM! IF I TREAT HIM LIKE A FRIEND, HE'LL STOP BEING SUCH A THUG!
IT SAYS SO RIGHT HERE IN THIS BOOK!
PAT PAT
CHESTER, MY MAN!
WHAM!
"UNDERSTANDING BULLIES"
HE'S A WORK IN PROGRESS.
Peirce

MAN! THIS SCIENCE REPORT IS GONNA BE TOUGH!
I HAVEN'T EVEN COME UP WITH MY HYPOTHESIS YET!
I HAVE!
AND WHAT IS IT?
I INTEND TO PROVE, ONCE AND FOR ALL, SCIENTIFICALLY, THAT DOGS ARE SMARTER THAN CATS!
WURF?
11/6
GOOD LUCK!
SPITSY, YOU IDIOT.
Peirce

SPARKY, SCRUFFY, SPANKY, TUFFY, REX, SUNNY, CHARLIE, JACK, BUCKY...
IN CASE MY DAD GETS ME A DOG FOR CHRISTMAS, I WANT TO HAVE A NAME ALL READY TO GO!
SMITTY, RUFUS, NEMO, BARKY, KID, WILLIE, DENNY, POKEY, LEFTY, TWITCHY...
12/22
© 2003 by NEA, Inc.
"TWITCHY"?
I'M PICTURING A CHIHUAHUA WITH ATTENTION DEFICIT DIS-ORDER!
Peirce

YOUR LOCKER'S PRETTY NASTY, NATE.
WHATTA YA MEAN?
WHAT DO I **MEAN**? YOU'RE WAIST-DEEP IN **TRASH**!
**TRASH**? EX**CUSE** ME, TEDDY, BUT THERE'S A LOT OF GOOD STUFF IN HERE!
...LIKE **THIS**!
AN AUTOGRAPHED PHOTO OF ABE LINCOLN?
I'M THINKING OF APPLYING FOR LANDMARK STATUS!
1/14
PEIRCE

HOW DOES MRS. GODFREY EXPECT US TO MEM-ORIZE ALL THESE DATES? THIS IS IMPOSSIBLE!
FOR ME, IT'S EASY!
YOU SEE, I HAVE A PHOTOGRAPHIC MEMORY!
PHOTOGRAPH THIS.
I TOOK THE PHOTO, BUT I WON'T BE ORDERING DOUBLE PRINTS.
2/25
Peirce

THERE GOES MARCUS WITH HIS POSSE.
YEAH. MARCUS IS COOL.
EXACTLY! AND WHY IS HE COOL? HE'S COOL BECAUSE HE HAS A POSSE!
4/12
UH...NO, HE HAS A POSSE BECAUSE HE'S COOL.
YEAH, YEAH, WHATEVER. THE POINT IS, I NEED A POSSE!
NO, THE POINT IS, YOU'RE NOT COOL.
KEEP TALKING, FRANCIS, AND I MIGHT NOT POSSE-FY YOU.
"POSSE-FY"?
© 2004 by NEA, Inc.
Peirce

HEY, WANT A FORTUNE COOKIE?
A FORTUNE COOKIE?
YEAH, WE WENT OUT FOR CHINESE FOOD LAST NIGHT!
THANKS.
"YOU SOMETIMES FAIL TO SEE THE FOREST FOR THE TREES."
5/23
*SPUTTER!* WHAT KIND OF FORTUNE IS THAT? THAT'S NO FORTUNE!
A FORTUNE IS SUPPOSED TO TELL THE FUTURE! THIS IS JUST SOME LAME SLOGAN!
IF YOU'RE GOING TO CALL 'EM FORTUNE COOKIES, PUT AN ACTUAL FORTUNE IN 'EM!
DON'T TELL ME "YOU CAN'T SEE THE FOREST FOR THE TREES"! TELL ME WHAT'S GOING TO HAPPEN!!
WAM!
HOW PAIN-FULLY IRONIC.
IT SHOULD HAVE SAID "THE FOREST OR THE TREES"!
PEIRCE

IT REALLY STEAMS ME THAT THE SCHOOL DISPLAY CASE IS DEVOTED ENTIRELY TO ARTUR AND GINA'S ACADEMIC AWARDS!
HOW COME IT'S ALL THEM? HOW COME I'M NOT IN THERE?
5/31
MMMF! SMIRK!
DO YOU WANT TO CONNECT THE DOTS FOR HIM, OR SHOULD I?
IT'S ALMOST CRUEL!
Peirce

OH, MAN, DID I GET SLAMMED ON THIS MATH TEST!
WHOA! YOU GOT A FIFTY-TWO?
I THOUGHT ONLY NATE GOT SCORES THAT LOW!
I GUESS I PULLED A NATE!
HEE HEE! YOU NATED IT!
YES! YES! I NATED IT!
HA HA HA HA
6/8
© 2004 by NEA, Inc.
I'VE BECOME A VERB.
YOU TOTALLY NATED IT!
HA HA HA HA HA HA
Peirce

UH-OH.
UH-OH WHAT?
HERE COMES THAT MEAN DOG FROM UP THE BLOCK.
I HEARD HE TRIED TO BITE HENRY LAST WEEK.
LET'S GO INSIDE.
YEAH.
HOLD ON, GUYS! I'VE GOT AN IDEA!
THIS'LL CALM THAT DOG DOWN!
7/25
MUSIC HATH CHARMS TO SOOTHE THE SAVAGE BEAST!
GRRRRRRRR
BLAAT!
YIP YIP YIP YIP YIP YIP YIP
"SOOTHE"?
"MUSIC"?
YOU'RE WELCOME.

WHAT'RE YOU DOING?
PAINTING.
BUT... IT'S BLANK!
OF COURSE IT'S BLANK, YOU IDIOT!
8/8
I'M AN ARTIST! AND, LIKE ALL ARTISTS, I CAN'T BE RUSHED!
I JUST CAN'T MINDLESSLY START PAINTING! I'M WAITING FOR A MOMENT OF ARTISTIC INSPIRATION!
I'M WAITING FOR SOMETHING TO HIT ME.
diff!
Peirce

HOW GOES THE PAINTING?
AWESOME!
AT FIRST, I DIDN'T KNOW WHAT TO PAINT! I WAS HAVING "ARTIST'S BLOCK"!
8/15
...BUT THEN I TOOK A LOOK AROUND! AT THE SKY... THE WATER... THE TREES... THE GRASS...
THE CLOUDS WERE FORMING THESE INCREDIBLE PATTERNS... BIRDS WERE FLYING AND SWOOPING ALL OVER THE PLACE...
SUDDENLY, I FELT TOTALLY IN TOUCH WITH MY SURROUNDINGS! I WAS ONE WITH NATURE!
THAT FEELING OF PEACE AND SERENITY IS WHAT ENABLED ME TO CREATE THE MASTERPIECE YOU SEE BEFORE YOU!
I CALL IT "BATTLE OF THE BLOODSUCKING BIKER BABES"!
LOVE THE BIKINIS!
Peirce

TWEET!
PENALTY KICK!
LET'S GO, NATE! EYE OF THE TIGER!
RIGHT! EYE OF THE TIGER!
EYE OF THE TIGER!
EYE OF THE TIGER!
WAM!
IT'S SWOLLEN SHUT.
NICE SAVE, TIGER!
FIRST AID

DANG!
8/29
WHAT?
THIS PEN IS TOO THIN.
TOO THIN?
I'M TRYING TO DRAW A COMIC STRIP AND IT LOOKS ALL WRONG.
LOOKS OK TO ME.
NO, IT DOESN'T! LOOK HOW SKINNY THE LINES ARE! YOU CAN BARELY SEE 'EM!
WHAT'S THE DIFF?
WHAT'S THE DIFF? IT LOOKS LOUSY, THAT'S WHAT!
SO STOP WHINING AND USE A DIF-FERENT PEN! HERE!
BETTER?
YOU'RE TOTALLY THICK, YOU KNOW THAT?
Peirce

HA HA HA HA HA
HEH HEH HA
HA HA HA
WHAT?
10
11
YOUR HAIR!
MY HAIR?
MMMPH!
WE... HA HA!... WE'D NEVER REALLY LOOKED AT IT BEFORE!
HA HA HA HA HEH HA HA HA HEH HA HA HA HA
WHAT'S SO FUNNY?
© 2004 by NEA, Inc.
HA HA HO H
HO HA HA HA
A HA
TIME TO MOVE TO A NEW TABLE.
Peirce

WHAT'S UP?
QUIET, TEDDY! I'M WAITING FOR FRANCIS!
HOW COME?
TO NAIL HIM WITH THIS SNOWBALL, THAT'S HOW COME!
HE AMBUSHED ME YESTERDAY, SO TODAY IT'S PAYBACK!
I'VE BEEN WAITING HERE FOR AN HOUR! THE TRAP IS READY TO BE SPRUNG!
AN HOUR?
SSH! HERE HE COMES!
1/16
HAR HAR!
?
POW!
AFTER AN HOUR IN SUB-FREEZING TEMPERATURES, A SNOWBALL TENDS TO STICK TO A WOOL MITTEN!
Peirce

IS NATE STILL TRYING TO SET A WORLD RECORD?
YEAH.
HE SAID SOMETHING ABOUT BUILDING THE WORLD'S LARGEST SNOWMAN.
2/25
© 2005 by NEA, Inc.
I HAD AN ACCIDENT.
IS THERE A WORLD RECORD FOR STUPIDITY?
Peirce

ARTUR! HOW 'BOUT A GAME OF CHESS?
HMM. AM NOT SURE, NATE.
OH, C'MON! JUST ONE GAME BETWEEN FRIENDS!
WAL... HOKAY. SINCE YOU PUT IT LIKE THAT WAY, HOKAY.
3/1
WILL PLAY ONE GAME BECAUSE YOU ARE MY CHUMP!
Peirce
© 2005 by NEA, Inc.
DID YOU JUST CALL ME YOUR "CHUMP," ARTUR?
YOU BETCHA!
I THINK HE MEANT "CHUM."

SAY YOU'RE MAROONED ON A DESERTED ISLAND...
OK...
YOU CAN ONLY HAVE **ONE** KIND OF FOOD AND **ONE** KIND OF LIQUID FOR THE REST OF YOUR LIFE. WHAT WOULD THEY BE?
HMMM...
WATER.
3/6
WATER?
IT'S THE MOST LOGICAL CHOICE. SUGARY DRINKS LIKE SODA AND PUNCH JUST MAKE YOU **MORE** THIRSTY!
NOW FOR THE **FOOD**, I'D NEED SOMETHING TO KEEP MY ENERGY UP, RIGHT? I'D NEED **PROTEIN**!... AND **VITAMINS**!
...SO I'D PROBABLY GO FOR A TOFU-VEGGIE BURGER, SOMETHING LIKE THAT.
A TOFU-VEGGIE BURGER.
AND WATER.
YUP
diff!
Peirce
OW!
A RESPONSE WAS CALLED FOR.
REMIND ME NOT TO GET MAROONED WITH MISTER "FOOD PYRAMID."

WHO DO YOU THINK IS THE COOLEST KID IN SCHOOL?
MARCUS. NO QUESTION.
YEAH. MARCUS.
WHY **MARCUS**? WHY NOT **ME**? I'M COOL TOO!
MARCUS IS COOL WITHOUT EVEN **TRYING**!
SO AM **I**! THAT'S EXACTLY THE WAY **I** AM!
5/2
© 2005 by NEA, Inc.
I **NEVER** TRY TO BE COOL!
...WHICH WOULD EXPLAIN QUITE A BIT!
YEAH, YOU'RE **GOOD**!
Peirce

KLIK!
FOOOOM!
LOOK AT THIS! WHAT A MESS!
NATE, YOUR LOCKER IS LIKE A TOXIC WASTE DUMP!
5/22
PEOPLE ARE SICK OF DEALING WITH YOUR JUNK! YOU'VE GOT TO DO SOMETHING ABOUT IT!
LIGHTEN UP, FRANCIS! I DID DO SOMETHING ABOUT IT!
I INSTALLED A VACUUM!
BZZZ!
WOOOOOOoo
SLAM!
FRANCIS?
HEY!
BAM!
BAM!

WELL, THIS IS THE FIRST ART OPENING I'VE EVER BEEN A PART OF! THE FIRST OF **MANY**, MIGHT I ADD!

I JUST WISH THEY WERE GIVING OUT **PRIZES!** I DON'T THINK THERE'S MUCH DOUBT ABOUT WHO'D GET THE BLUE RIBBON!

I MEAN, NO OFFENSE TO THE REST OF YOU, BUT I THINK IT'S CLEAR WHO'S THE MOST TALENTED ARTIST AT THIS OPENING!
6/7
© 2005 by NEA, Inc.
SPEAKING OF OPENINGS, HOW ABOUT SHUTTING THAT BIG ONE IN THE MIDDLE OF YOUR FACE?
WHOA, TEDDY, WHOA. THAT'S THE MOUNTAIN DEW TALKING.
Peirce

I LET A FROG LOOSE IN MR. GALVIN'S ROOM!
I PUT A WHOOPEE CUSHION ON MS. LA CHANCE'S CHAIR!
I SCANNED MRS. GODFREY'S HEAD ONTO THE BODY OF A SUMO WRESTLER, THEN SENT THE PICTURE TO EVERY COMPUTER IN THE SCHOOL DISTRICT DISGUISED AS AN URGENT MEMO FROM THE SUPERINTENDENT.
WE'RE IN THE PRESENCE OF "PRANK DAY" GREATNESS.
AMATEUR HOUR IS OVER, BOYS.
6/17
Peirce

TEDDY, LOOK! SOMEBODY FOUND A CAT!
HEY, ISN'T THAT NATE'S PHONE NUMBER?
FOUND CAT
YOU'RE RIGHT! IT IS!
SO NATE'S FAMILY HAS A CAT?
7/7
NATE AND A CAT LIVING IN THE SAME HOUSE?
BACK! BACK, FOUL BEAST!
MYOWR!
PEIRCE
© 2005 by NEA, Inc.

ONE, PLEASE.
Lemonade 50¢
SMACK!
HEY, THIS JUST TASTES LIKE **WATER**!
READ THE FINE PRINT.
"NO LEMONS WERE HARMED DURING THE MAKING OF THIS PRODUCT."
8/22
© 2005 by NEA, Inc.
WHAT THE...?
IT'S GUILT-FREE!
Peirce

FIRST AND TEN!
OKAY, ARTUR. HUDDLE UP.
I'LL BE Q.B.... YOU GO OUT.
HOKAY. GO OUT WHERE?
GO OUT FOR A PASS! DO A BUTTON-HOOK!
WHAT IS BUTTON-HOOK?
YOU JUST GO UP THE FIELD, AND...
WHAT FIELD I GO TO?
THE FIELD, ARTUR! THE FIELD WE'RE PLAYING ON!
BUT ON STREET WE ARE PLAYING.
OKAY, THEN! WHATEVER! YOU GO UP THE STREET!
TAKE FIVE STEPS, TURN AROUND, AND LOOK FOR THE BALL!
I SEE BALL ALREADY! IS RIGHT THERE!
8/28
NO! I MEAN LOOK FOR THE PASS WHEN YOU GO OUT!
YES. GO OUT WHERE?
Peirce
JUST GET OPEN!
I'LL BET WE WIN.
IF WE EVER PLAY.

OH NO. IT'S GINA.
GROAN...
HI GUYS! CAN I JOIN YOU?
UHH...
SURE, GINA! WE'D LOVE TO HAVE YOU!...
...BUT WOULDN'T YOU RATHER SIT WITH MRS. GODFREY? SHE'S UNDER THAT RED UMBRELLA!
SHE IS?
YOO HOO!
HIGH FIVE!
I KNOW MY SUCK-UPS.
9/1
© 2005 by NEA, Inc.
Peirce

GENTS! I THOUGHT YOU WERE DOWN AT THE POND!
WE WERE, UNTIL SOME STUPID FIGURE SKATERS STARTED HOG-GING THE ICE!
BUT YOU LIKE FIGURE SKATING, DON'T YOU? DIDN'T YOU SEND A FAN LETTER TO MICHELLE KWAN?
SASHA COHEN.
I MEAN... UH... WHAT? NO!... WHO?
BUSTED!
© 2006 by NEA, Inc.
2 9
Peirce

YOU'RE SO SHALLOW, NATE!
YEAH, ALL YOU CARE ABOUT IS BEING FAMOUS SOMEDAY!
SHALLOW?
I'M NOT SHALLOW! I'M DEEP, BROTHER! I'M CHOCK-FULL OF DEEP THOUGHTS!
4/11
DEEP THOUGHTS? LIKE WHAT?
WELL, I... *SPUTTER!* I CAN'T JUST COME UP WITH SOMETHING OFF THE TOP OF MY HEAD! THAT'S NOT HOW DEEPNESS WORKS!
"DEEP-NESS"?
DON'T YOU MEAN "DEPTH", PINHEAD?
QUIET. I'M THINKING.
Peirce

DO YOU THINK GIRLS RATE US?
HM?
5/22
I MEAN, WE RATE THEM, RIGHT? I'M WONDERING IF THEY RATE US THE SAME WAY!
PSST! PSST!
WHISPER!
PSST!
HA HA HA HA HA H HA HA
© 2006 by NEA, Inc.
APPARENTLY SO.
HA HA HA HA HA HA H EWWWW! HA HA HA
Peirce

WELL, "PRANK DAY" WILL BE PRETTY UNEVENTFUL **THIS** YEAR.
DON'T BE SO SURE, LADS!
WHAT? NATE, YOU HEARD GODFREY YESTERDAY!
YEAH, SHE MEANT BUSINESS! NO JOKES, NO PRANKS, **NOTHING**!
6/13
YOU'RE NOT GOING TO DO ANYTHING STUPID, ARE YOU?
OOP! HOLD IT! HANG ON!
WHY EVEN ASK?
GUYS, **CHILL**! SETTLE DOWN IN THERE!
PEIRCE

WHAT'S WITH **YOU**?
I STAYED UP WATCHING TV UNTIL THREE A.M.
WHY?
WHY? BECAUSE IT.. SUMMER! JUNE! LATE! CAN'T!
6/29
JUST!... DARK!... FOO!... WUB!... SCHNEE!... YIP!
© 2006 by NEA, Inc.
THEY SAY SLEEP-DEPRIVED PEOPLE ARE OFTEN NONSENSICAL.
WHAT ABOUT ALL THE TIMES HE'S **NOT** SLEEP-DEPRIVED?
OPRAH!
Peirce

TA-DAAH!
WHAT IS THAT?
IT'S A SELF-PORTRAIT, OBVIOUSLY!
IT'S A SAND SCULPTURE OF YOURS TRULY! SO NOW THERE ARE TWO OF ME!
7/22
peirce
© 2006 by NEA, Inc.
ISN'T ONE OF YOU ENOUGH?
AMEN, BROTHER.
HEY, GUYS, I'M BESIDE MYSELF!
CHUCKLE

THIS HAS GOT TO BE THE HOTTEST DAY OF THE YEAR.
8/21
YOU'RE RIGHT.
FOOSSH!
HUMID, TOO.
PERSONALLY, I FEEL REFRESHED!
© 2006 by NEA, Inc.
Peirce

LAST DAY OF SUMMER VACATION! WHAT SHOULD WE DO?
9/4
I DON'T KNOW, BUT DOWN THE ROAD THE WEATHER GODS OWE US BIG TIME.

I DON'T GET IT. WHY IS ARTUR AL-WAYS SO **NICE** TO ME?
BECAUSE HE'S A NICE KID, THAT'S WHY!

BUT WHY WASTE YOUR TIME BEING NICE TO SOMEONE WHO CAN'T **STAND** YOU? WHAT'S UP WITH **THAT**?

WELL, SOME PEOPLE...
OOP! HOLD ON!
9/13

JENNY, M'LADY!
SOME PEOPLE ARE JUST KIND OF CLUE-LESS.
Peirce

LET'S SAY YOU JUST FOUND OUT YOU HAVE ONLY 24 HOURS TO LIVE. WHAT WOULD YOU DO?
HOW WOULD YOU SPEND YOUR LAST DAY ON EARTH?
WELL, THAT WOULD DEPEND ON WHAT DAY IT WAS.
WHY WOULD IT MATTER?
IT WOULD MATTER IF IT WAS A SUNDAY. SUNDAY'S MY TV NIGHT.
OF COURSE, IF "FAMILY GUY" WAS A RERUN, THAT WOULD BE A DIFFERENT STORY.
9/15
Peirce

FAKE LEFT, THEN RUN A FADE TO THE RIGHT CORNER.
GOTCHA!
HIKE!
THINK YOU CAN COVER ME, FRANCIS? HA!
NOT WITH THIS BURST OF SPEED!
I'M OPEN!! I'M WIDE OPEN!!
10/29
GAAAA
TRIP!
YOU BEAT THE CORNERBACK, BUT YOU COULDN'T BEAT THE SAFETY!
NO, BUT I'M GOING TO SMASH HIM LATER.
PAT! PAT!

ACCORDING TO THIS ARTICLE, WOMEN ARE ATTRACTED TO "BAD BOYS"!
COSMO
THERE'S SOMETHING ABOUT A REBEL THAT THE LADIES FIND IRRESISTIBLE! HMMM!...
COSMO
11/6
GENTS, I DO BELIEVE I'M GETTING ANOTHER BRILLIANT IDEA!
"ANOTHER"?
YUP! THE HITS JUST KEEP ON COMIN'!
Peirce

NATE! WHAT'S WITH THE GREASER LOOK?
JUST PART OF MY NEW "BAD BOY" IMAGE!
I GOT THE IDEA FROM THAT ARTICLE I READ ABOUT WOMEN BEING ATTRACTED TO REBELS!
11/7
POINK!
POINK!
POINK!
YOUR HAIR IS CERTAINLY REBELLIOUS!
DANG! THERE GOES A WHOLE TUBE OF DIPPITY-DO!
POINK!
POINK!
POINK!
Peirce
© 2006 by NEA, Inc.

A LEATHER JACKET?
HE'S A "BAD BOY".
11/8
YOU'RE ACTUALLY FOLLOWING THROUGH ON THAT DUMB IDEA?
DUMB IDEA? IT'S RIGHT HERE IN BLACK AND WHITE!
"FOR A MULTITUDE OF REASONS, WOMEN ARE OFTEN ATTRACTED TO 'BAD BOYS' – MEN WHO SIMPLY AREN'T GOOD FOR THEM."
COSMO
© 2006 by NEA, Inc.
THAT'S YOU, ALL RIGHT!
YEAH, YOU'RE GOOD FOR **NOTHING**!
HI, LADIES.
Peirce

JENNY! CHECK IT OUT! I'M A "BAD BOY"!
A WHAT?
A BAD BOY! I'M DANGEROUS, BABY! I'M BAD TO THE BONE!
YOU?
HA HA HA HA
HA HA HA HA HA
HA HA HA
11 9
I'M HAVING TROUBLE GETTING MY BADNESS ACROSS.
WELL, THERE'S A DIF- FERENCE BETWEEN "BAD" AND "LAME."
PEIRCE

WHAT'S UP, LADIES?
UH... NOTHING.
HEY! WE DIDN'T INVITE YOU TO SIT WITH US!
INVITE ME? LISTEN, I'M A "BAD BOY"!
I SIT WHEREVER I WANT TO SIT!
...AND RIGHT ABOUT NOW, THE COT IN THE NURSE'S OFFICE SOUNDS PRETTY GOOD.
© 2006 by NEA, Inc.
11/10
Peirce

FAKE FIGHT?
FAKE FIGHT!
POW!
OOF!
HYA!
ARRGH!
BOOF!
CHUCKLE!
FOOM!
HEY!
YOU CLIPPED ME FOR REAL!
OW!
SHOVE!
DON'T PUNK ME, MAN!
YOU STARTED IT, SCRUB!
LOOKS LIKE FUN, DOESN'T IT?
IF YOU SAY SO.
OW! I'M BLEEDING, YOU JERK!
JERK THIS, WUSSY BOY!
PEIRCE

GAH! MY DAD PACKED ME TURKEY AGAIN!
JEFF! WANNA TRADE LUNCHES?
ALL I'VE GOT IS THANKSGIVING LEFTOVERS.
11/28
ME TOO, BUT WE CAN...
LIVER PATÉ ON CABBAGE LEAVES, CHILLED OYSTER SOUP, TOFU KABOBS, AND A THERMOS OF PRUNE JUICE.
© 2006 by NEA, Inc.
REMIND ME NOT TO ATTEND ANY HOLIDAY PARTIES AT JEFF'S HOUSE.
PEIRCE

I DON'T THINK I'LL EAT TURKEY AGAIN AS LONG AS I LIVE!
BY MAKING ME EAT SO MUCH OF IT, MY DAD HAS RUINED A PERFECTLY GOOD FOOD FOR ME!
12/2
I ONCE THREW UP AFTER EATING A BUNCH OF GUMMI BEARS AND NOW I, LIKE, TOTALLY HATE GUMMI BEARS.
© 2006 by NEA, Inc.
THANKS, TEDDY. WHAT A FASCINATING ADDITION TO THE DISCUSSION.
ONE BEAR CAME OUT MY NOSE.
Peirce

GOOD MORN~
DIBS.
HUH?
I CALLED DIBS.
ON WHAT?
ON EVERY-THING. FOREVER.
WAIT A MINUTE!
YOU'RE IN MY SEAT.
© 2006 by NEA, Inc.

MRS. GODFREY SAYS THAT IF I DON'T START KEEPING MY DESK AND LOCKER CLEAN, IT'LL AFFECT MY GRADE!
BETTER NEATEN UP, DUDE.
I CAN'T! I'VE TRIED, BUT I CAN'T!
I'M JUST A MESSY PERSON! I WAS BORN MESSY!
WELL, TECHNIC-ALLY, I THINK EVERY-ONE'S BORN MESSY.
© 2007 by NEA, Inc.
YEAH, REMEMBER THAT MOVIE WE SAW IN HEALTH CLASS?
CAN WE TALK ABOUT SOME-THING ELSE?

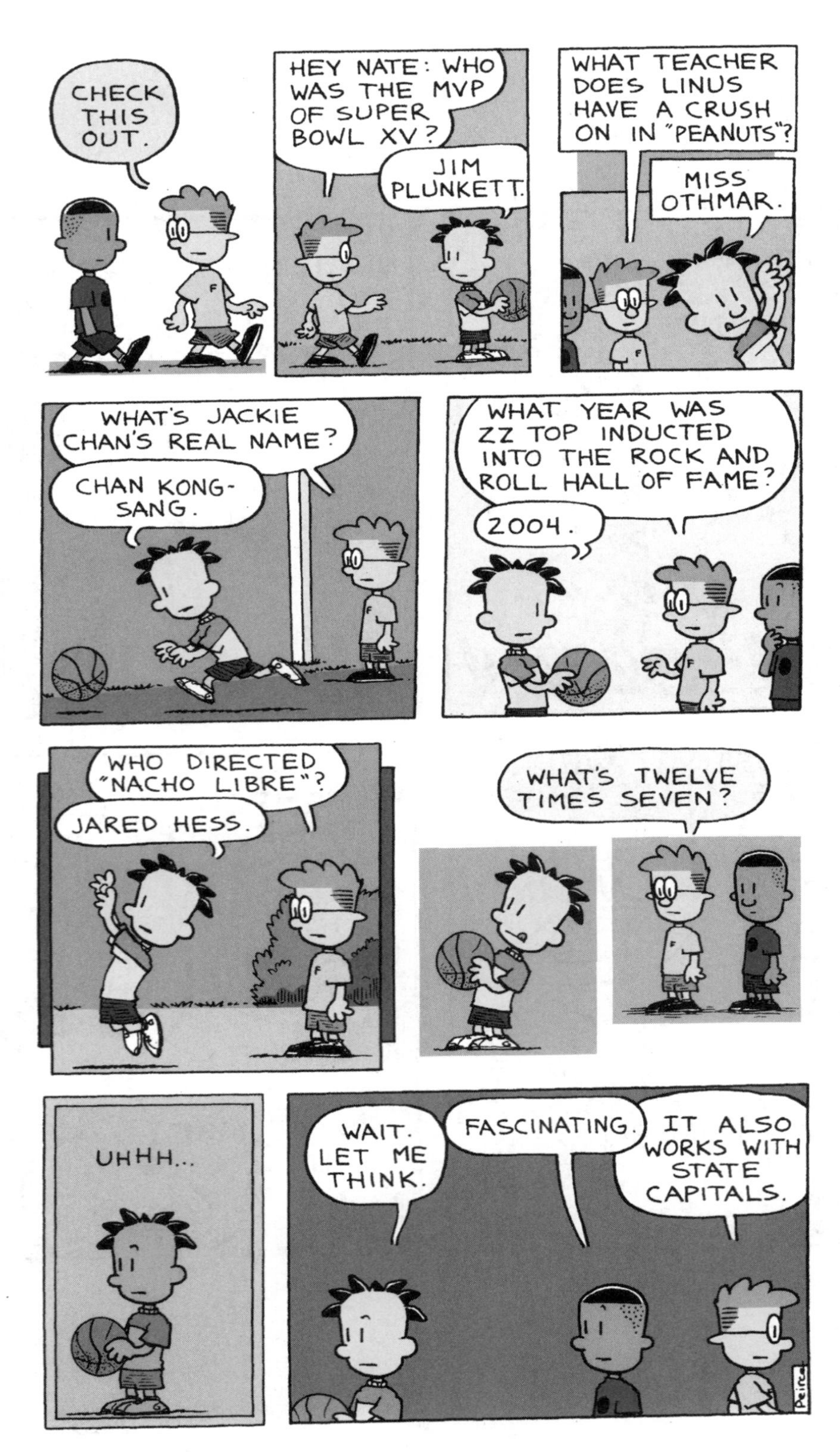
CHECK THIS OUT.
HEY NATE: WHO WAS THE MVP OF SUPER BOWL XV?
JIM PLUNKETT.
WHAT TEACHER DOES LINUS HAVE A CRUSH ON IN "PEANUTS"?
MISS OTHMAR.
WHAT'S JACKIE CHAN'S REAL NAME?
CHAN KONG-SANG.
WHAT YEAR WAS ZZ TOP INDUCTED INTO THE ROCK AND ROLL HALL OF FAME?
2004.
WHO DIRECTED "NACHO LIBRE"?
JARED HESS.
WHAT'S TWELVE TIMES SEVEN?
UHHH...
WAIT. LET ME THINK.
FASCINATING.
IT ALSO WORKS WITH STATE CAPITALS.
Peirce

SUMMER VACATION STARTS IN TWENTY SECONDS!
WHAT SHOULD WE DO FIRST?
I'M GOING ON A DIET!
A DIET?
YUP! I'M ABOUT TO LOSE... OH, I'D SAY AROUND FIFTEEN POUNDS!
WUMP!
KEEP OUR SCHOO CLEA
RRRRIINNGG!!
6/23

I THINK NOT.
SAME HERE.
AHHHHH, VACATION!
© 2007 by NEA, Inc.
6
27
Peirce

"POOR NATE'S ALMANAC"? WHAT'S THIS?
I'M FOLLOWING IN THE FOOTSTEPS OF BEN FRANKLIN, BOYS!
POOR NATE'S ALMANAC $2
BACK IN THE 1700S, OL' BEN PUBLISHED "POOR RICHARD'S ALMANACK"!
IT WAS FILLED WITH ALL SORTS OF WISE SAYINGS LIKE "THE EARLY BIRD GETS THE WORM" AND "A PENNY SAVED IS A PENNY EARNED"!
"POOR NATE'S ALMANAC" IS THE SAME THING, ONLY **BETTER**! YOU WON'T BELIEVE ALL THE WISDOM IN HERE!
AND THESE ARE MY LAST TWO COPIES! A BARGAIN AT TWO BUCKS EACH!
OKAY, I'LL TAKE ONE.
ME TOO!
HEY! THIS THING'S **BLANK**!
WAIT, THERE'S SOMETHING WRITTEN ON THE LAST PAGE.
FLIP FLIP FLIP
There's a sucker born every minute.
PEIRCE

WHAT ARE YOU DOING?
DIGGING UP MY TIME CAPSULE, FRANCIS!
CHOP CHOP CHOP CHOP CHOP CHOP
REMEMBER WHEN WE MADE TIME CAPSULES BACK IN THIRD GRADE? WELL, I BURIED MINE **RIGHT HERE!**
CHOP CHOP CHOP CHOP CHOP CHOP
CHUNK!
8/20
...OR IS THIS WHERE I BURIED MY HAMSTER?
EWW.
Peirce

DO YOU THINK TEACHERS EVER HANG OUT TOGETHER OUTSIDE OF SCHOOL?
WHY WOULDN'T THEY?
WELL, THEY PROBABLY GET SICK OF EACH OTHER, WORKING IN THE SAME BUILDING ALL YEAR LONG, RIGHT?
WHY HANG OUT WITH SOMEBODY YOU'RE SICK OF?
HARDY HAR HAR!
© 2007 by NEA, Inc.
9/13
Peirce

I'LL COVER!
AND I'LL RUSH!
WHAT'S THE RUSH COUNT? FIVE MISSISSIPPI?
WHATEVER. DOESN'T MATTER.
DOESN'T MATTER?
RUSH WHENEVER YOU WANT.
THREE MISSISSIPPI, THEN!
SURE.
TWO MISSISSIPPI!
OKAY.
HIKE!
ONE MISSISSIPPI...
...TWO MISSISSIPPI!
FSSST!
GAH!
FLING!
MY MOM WAS THROWING OUT SOME PERFUME!
OOH! WHO SMELLS DREAMY?
Peirce

REMEMBER THAT BAND THAT PLAYED AT THE SPRING DANCE?
"THE DIS-TEMPERS"?
WHAT ABOUT THEM?
WELL, THEY WERE JUST A BUNCH OF HIGH SCHOOL KIDS, RIGHT? WHY COULDN'T **WE** DO THAT?
9/24
**I** COULD DO EVERYTHING THAT **THEIR** LEAD SINGER DID!
I TOTALLY AGREE!...
...ESPECIALLY THE PART WHERE HE SNEEZED DURING "STAIRWAY TO HEAVEN," THEN FELL OFF THE STAGE!
YEAH, THAT IS **SO** YOU!
© 2007 by NEA, Inc.
PEIRCE

SAY WE DO DECIDE TO START A BAND. HOW DO WE DO IT?
WE JUST... DO IT!
ALL WE HAVE TO DO IS SAY "WE'RE A BAND" AND WE'RE A BAND!
OKAY! WE'RE A BAND!
NOW WHAT?
THIS IS BORING.
PATIENCE, MEN. I'LL WHIP UP A PRESS RELEASE.
Peirce 9/27

WHAT'S YOUR FAVORITE MOVIE?
I DUNNO.
YOU DON'T KNOW?
I HAVEN'T GIVEN IT MUCH THOUGHT.
WELL, WHAT ABOUT SONGS? WHAT'S YOUR FAVORITE SONG?
I LIKE LOTS OF SONGS.
BUT WHICH ONE DO YOU LIKE BEST?
I HAVE NO IDEA.
OKAY, THEN, COLORS! EVERYONE HAS A FAVORITE COLOR!
NOT ME.
OH, COME ON, FRANCIS! THERE'S GOT TO BE A COLOR YOU LIKE! JUST PICK ONE!
KLUNK!
SPLOOSH!
RED.
PEIRCE

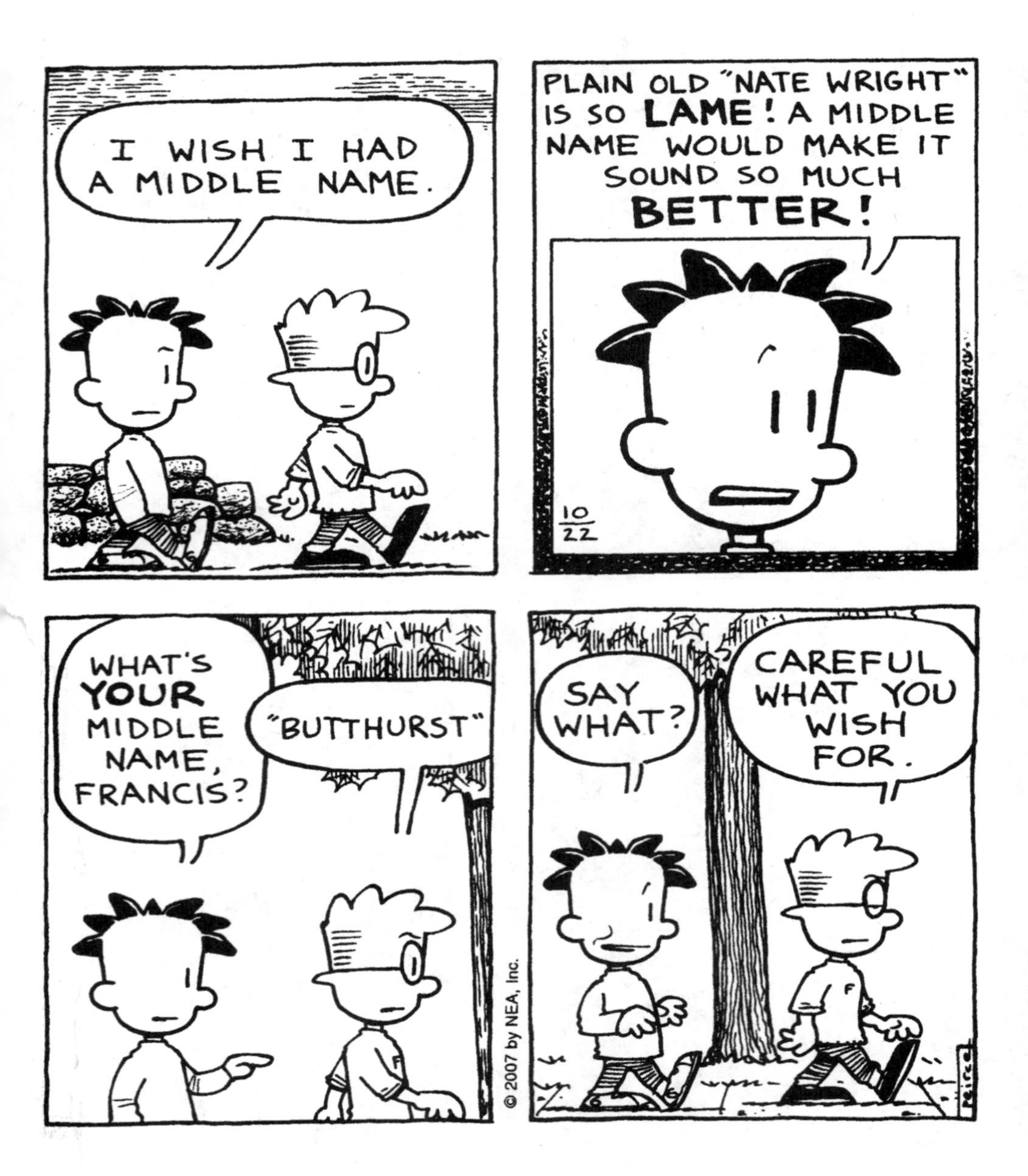
I WISH I HAD A MIDDLE NAME.
PLAIN OLD "NATE WRIGHT" IS SO LAME! A MIDDLE NAME WOULD MAKE IT SOUND SO MUCH BETTER!
10/22
WHAT'S YOUR MIDDLE NAME, FRANCIS?
"BUTTHURST"
SAY WHAT?
CAREFUL WHAT YOU WISH FOR.

IS IT TRUE YOU DON'T HAVE A MIDDLE NAME?
YUP.
THAT'S WEIRD, DUDE.
WHAT'S YOURS?
√‾‾
10
23
THAT'S WEIRD, DUDE.
MY PARENTS ARE MATH TEACHERS.
Peirce

DAD, YOU KNOW HOW I DON'T HAVE A MIDDLE NAME?
MM.
WELL, CAN I THINK ONE UP FOR MYSELF?
MM.
I CAN?
WAIT!... WHAT?
"FUNKMEISTER"!
10/24
© 2007 by NEA, Inc.
Peirce

GOOD NEWS, GUYS! MY DAD'S LETTING ME THINK UP A MIDDLE NAME FOR MYSELF!
I'M STILL MULLING IT OVER, BUT A CLEAR FRONT-RUNNER HAS EMERGED!
LET'S HEAR IT.
"MAXIMUS"!
VERY MODEST.
IS THAT A NAME OR A MALE ENHANCEMENT SUPPLEMENT?
10/25
Peirce

GUYS, HELP ME PICK OUT A GOOD MIDDLE NAME!
I'VE NARROWED IT DOWN TO CAESAR, SOLOMON, ARTHUR, ALEXANDER...
...AUGUSTUS, ZEUS, CONSTANTINE, HENRY, CHARLEMAGNE, AND JUSTINIAN!
10/26
I'M DETECTING A THEME.
EVER HEARD THE PHRASE, "NAPOLEON COMPLEX"?
OOH, NAPOLEON! THAT'S A GOOD ONE!

I'VE DECIDED TO STOP LOOKING FOR A MIDDLE NAME.
"NATE WRIGHT" IS A SIMPLE NAME, BUT SOMETIMES LESS IS MORE! SOMETIMES SIMPLE IS GOOD!
10 27
A SIMPLE NAME FOR A SIMPLE PERSON?
EXACTLY!
EXACTLY.
Peirce
© 2007 by NEA, Inc.

YOU KNOW WHAT, TEDDY? FRANCIS DOESN'T HAVE A FAVORITE MOVIE.
YOU DON'T?
THAT'S WEIRD, DUDE.
THAT'S WHAT I SAID!
WHY IS THAT SO WEIRD?
MOST PEOPLE HAVE A FAVORITE MOVIE, THAT'S ALL.
EVERY-BODY DOES!
OKAY, OKAY! IF IT'S THAT IMPORTANT, I'LL PICK ONE!
MY FAVORITE MOVIE IS "CASABLANCA"! SATISFIED?
OH, YEAH! THE ONE WITH THOSE ZOO ANIMALS?
...AND THEY WIND UP IN AFRICA!
NO, NO, NO! THAT'S "MADAGASCAR"!
"CASABLANCA" IS A CLASSIC! THE AMERICAN FILM INSTI-TUTE RANKS IT THE SECOND GREATEST FILM OF ALL TIME!
HUH.
NEVER HEARD OF IT.
MY FAVORITE IS "DUMB AND DUMBER"!
HEY! SAME HERE!
REMEMBER HARRY'S BATHROOM SCENE?
HILARIOUS!
HERE'S LOOKING AT YOU, KID.
Peirce